W9-DEW-846

What people are saying about
The Inspired Business Toolkit...

As a serial entrepreneur, many women ask me to recommend a book to help them jumpstart their business and their dream. Frankly, I've never been able to find it all in one book. Until now.

The *Inspired Business Toolkit* doesn't just cover marketing plans and mission statements, it covers the really important things like self-sabotage, permission to say no, and letting go of perfection.

Owning a business can be lonely. Diane's book will make you feel like you've got a friend who's walking along beside you all the way.

Cheryl Karpen, Gently Spoken, Home of the Eat Your Peas Collection, www.gentlyspoken.com

~~~~~

Diane doesn't miss a thing! In her book *The Inspired Business Toolkit* she guides you through everything from creating your mission statement to analyzing your niche. A great resource and guide for any entrepreneur.

Michelle Prince, America's Productivity Coach
Www.MichellePrince.com

~~~~~

The Inspired Business Toolkit is a fantastic resource for everyone who is serious about building their business! The wealth of practical tips and insights make it a must read. Thank you, Diane, for this incredible work!

J. Nicole Williamson, King's Lantern Publishing
www.kingslantern.com

~~~~~

If you are a woman embarking on a journey of starting your own business, you need this *The Inspired Business Toolkit*! Diane Cunningham is a woman of action who will help you achieve your goals fast and with focus. Through her own years of experience with the ups and downs of starting and running a business, she holds nothing back and shares with you everything she has learned along the journey so you won't have to make the same mistakes she has made. Diane is also on the cutting edge of new business technology and best practices. She is an inspired woman of passion and purpose and genuinely desires to see you succeed.

Kristi Olson, Life Purpose Strategist www.purposereleased.com

~~~~~

Diane's *Inspired Business Toolkit* is certain to dig out your brilliance and wisdom from the deepest recesses of your soul to not only allow you to bring forth your life purpose, but to actually enjoy creating a business that serves others around that purpose.

Camille Gains, CEO of the www.financialwoman.com

~~~~~

© 2010-2013 Diane Cunningham Companies LLC

This book can really help put someone in the right direction. On top of that Diane is truly an inspired woman and has the ability to inspire others as well. When starting a new entrepreneurial venture that is exactly what everyone needs.

Tereson Dupuy, Founder and Creator of www.fizzibunz.com

~~~~~

Wow! Diane - this book is amazing! I wish I had had something like this when I was just getting started in my business - and even last year! Come to think of it, the material in here will help women entrepreneurs at every level and in every stage of their businesses......I love it! I know I will use parts of this book over and over and over again....love the worksheets!!!!

Stephanie Ellis Ecke, LPC, LCDC www.thetraumaqueen.com

~~~~~

I LOVE it! Even though I've been building my SendOutCards business for a few years now, I feel like I would like to do more, but I don't know where to start. The toolkit will help women like me focus on their passions and pursue their dreams. I have the basic entrepreneurial skills down, but I need to find the focus that God is leading me towards. Thank you so much for creating such an inspirational product. I have no doubt that it will help a lot of women get beyond their fears and take action!

Karen Palmer with SendOutCards at www.worryfreemom.com

© 2010-2013 Diane Cunningham Companies LLC

The Inspired Business Toolkit

Diane Cunningham

Revised and Updated April 2013

The Inspired Business Toolkit

Copyright © 2010-2013 by Diane Cunningham

All rights reserved. No portion of this book may be reproduced, stored in any retrieval system, or transmitted in any form by any means- electronic, mechanical, photocopy, recording, or any other- except brief quotations in printed reviews, without the prior written permission of the authors and/or publisher.

All stories are used by permission. Internet addresses listed in the stories and bios are provided only as a resource- I cannot vouch for the content of these sites for the life of *The Inspired Business Toolkit book.*

Requests for information should be addressed to:

info@nacwe.org

Additional copies of this book are available at www.nacwe.org

ISBN: 9 781938 579943

Cover design by Sam Baja www.sambaja.com

© 2010-2013 Diane Cunningham Companies LLC

Acknowledgements

Gratitude is what I feel. This book has been a journey and a process. It has been a part of me for years and now getting out into the world. I am in awe.

God, thank you for the gift of writing and storytelling as a part of how we learn. Thank you for the gift of a business that you gave me in bits and pieces and long before I could recognize what I was holding. I pray that you multiply this book and expand it to reach the women you want it to reach. I pray that you give them to courage to step out in faith and hang out a shingle!

To my family, thank you for the ways you have always taught me. Each of us "teach" as a profession but it looks different for all of us. Thank you Dad for always modeling that education was crucial and encouraging me to go after my dreams! Thank you Mom for being the official "NACWE mom" and never once doubting that I could do all that I set out to do. Thank you to my dear younger sisters and the rest of the crew, who show me how to play and rest when we have our adventures.

To my friends, you have been my life line, my funny bone, my rescue team over the years. I have so many of you, both near and far, that I love. I cannot do this without you. You give me courage when I am in the middle of "crazyville" and you talk me off the ledge. I take you with me wherever I go and I feel strong.

To my NACWE sisters, this book is for you. It was for you before I ever met you because I could hear your heart cry. This book is our book. It is filled with your stories, quotes, truth, and wisdom. I salute you. And I love you. You are my inspiration to always keep going no matter how tired I feel or what obstacles may get in my way.

To my coaches and mentors, thank you for holding the sacred space for me to walk across each bridge. Thank you for pointing me back in the right direction each time I got distracted from the bigger goal. Thank you for showing me my VALUE and loving me until I could see it for myself. I am so blessed.

To my successes and failures, thank you for each lesson learned. I can look to you and see myself growing. I can see each stepping stone. I can feel each mistake. I can celebrate each victory and look back at the girl that I was before now. I know she is still ME. I am all of it. I am walking the path today and know that I will meet you both again as I succeed and as I fail. I am ready.

My prayer is that this book blesses you as you chase your dreams!

© 2010-2013 Diane Cunningham Companies LLC

Inspired Business Toolkit

Table of Contents

Go to www.nacwe.org/ToolkitResources for an online library of templates to accompany this book. Use the coupon code: *success* when you are checking out to receive your FREE GIFT!

© 2010-2013 Diane Cunningham Companies LLC

Forward

Many things have happened since the first writing of this tool-kit in 2010. We have been busy building and expanding at the National Association of Christian Women Entrepreneurs®, as we added members, connected with experts, and talked hourly in our private online forum.

Take a look at what we have been doing:

- During our first full year, NACWE welcomed 165 members
- In April 2011, right before our 1st year birthday, we hosted a National Conference in Dallas, Texas with 45 women in attendance. We are preparing for the next one in the Fall of 2013.
- During February of 2011, we invited 40 women to share their personal stories of transformation in the book Inspired Women Succeed
- We hosted a Virtual Conference in April 2012 with 8 webinars and 56 women connecting for 3 days

At the time of this revision of the Inspired Business Toolkit, we are growing and expanding as God leads. What a miracle and a blessing!

I have learned so much, made so many mistakes, and experienced so many God moments.....it is hard to capture them all in words.

As an entrepreneur, your personal life is also a part of your business. In March of 2011, I survived a plane crash which I now speak about across the country at events. And later that year I walked through the ending of my 10 year marriage. Needless to say, there have been many highs and many lows.

During each, NACWE has been here. The women of NACWE are my soul sisters, my comrades for the battle, my running partners, my prayer warriors, my dinner dates, and my business advisors. We are each unique, with varied skills, talents, business training, and locations. All of us come with personal challenges, family dynamics, and life baggage. But we meet in the middle each day in our forum, a place of love, support, acceptance, discovery, and celebration.

As you use this toolkit, the main thing I want you to know is that....YOU ARE NOT ALONE! I created NACWE, this toolkit, and everything else to help you to hear that, feel that, and know that. We are here for you. I am here for you! And we "get it"!

We are using our God-given gifts, learning each day, making mistakes, and loving each other through it. I hope and pray that this toolkit is a blessing to you!

With love and prayers,

Diane Cunningham

Go to www.nacwe.org/ToolkitResources to get your FREE gifts from me.....47 templates that go along with this book.
Use the coupon code: success

   © 2010-2013 Diane Cunningham Companies LLC

What is the Inspired Business Toolkit?

Welcome! My name is Diane Cunningham and I am so glad you are here with me. This book is a guide and resource for the Christian woman entrepreneur. I created it for you, page by page.

Each topic was selected on purpose. Each module is full of key concepts. Imagine an image of a puzzle that I have been creating over my lifetime. To build this puzzle, I looked back on how I built my business and how I help other women to build their dream into a business. Now it is all together and I can see the bigger picture. The puzzle is complete. We will use this toolkit as you build your puzzle. We will look for the right pieces, knowing that we will find some quickly and others seem to be hiding in plain view.

I am guessing that you are here for a few reasons. You most likely want a dose of **inspiration**. You might need more **information**. As you move through the process you will enjoy and experience **innovation**. You have a BIG DREAM and really no idea of the steps to get you there. You are just like me....A woman called by God to live out her purpose and all of a sudden you realize that means you might be opening a business. That is when you wonder what in the world you are doing and you begin to question your sanity.

You might be like I was....with "no business being in business"! I am a former counselor. I learned to sit and listen. I did not learn how to market or promote.   I have learned about marketing by putting myself "back in school" with trainings, retreats, workshops, and by just getting out there and doing it. When God gives you a plan and a purpose, you can truly learn anything. This book is for you. It is everything that I have learned in the 8 years since I officially hung my heart out on a shingle as a coach and speaker.

I trust that there will be all varieties of women using this toolkit. There will be those of you with just a dream, a crazy idea, who have not done a single thing yet. There will be others of you who I might call seasoned business women. Maybe you started your business years ago and now you find yourself needing to start over, rebrand, or start something completely new. Or you might be somewhere in the middle and know that you need a "tune-up".

I welcome all of you and we are all in this together. We work for the same boss.... God. When one of us succeeds, it helps all of us to succeed. I believe in the power of women to change the world. I believe in you and promise to help you build your dream in every way that I can, while teaching you all that I know.

So you might be wondering....

What is included in
The Inspired Business Toolkit?

Case Studies: Watch for case studies, stories and quotes from real women who are right in the middle of the journey.

Templates: The templates provide a place to get clarity and thus make better decisions.

Quizzes: Each quiz is focused on an area that might be impacting your business.

Information: Throughout the toolkit you will have definitions, tips, mind-set shifts, and observations from the path.

Lists: You will find both lists of information and checklists for

© 2010-2013 Diane Cunningham Companies LLC

you to fill out.

Resources: I love books, websites, and any tool that can help me so I will be sharing all of those with you too.

But let's go back to the basics...

Why do we need Inspiration?

I love the word inspiration. It makes me happy.

Inspiration is the arousal of the mind to special unusual activity or creativity and/or divine guidance or influence exerted directly on the mind and soul of human kind.

God is the provider of inspiration and He has given you a purpose. We know that "with God all things are possible". ~Matthew 19:26

Inspiration gives you courage.

Inspiration gives you vision.

Inspiration gives you drive.

Inspiration from God is anointed.

My favorite quote is this: Catch on fire with enthusiasm and people will come for miles to watch you burn. –John Wesley

Are you on fire?

What is your Business?

What is God telling you to do? I remember very loudly telling my best friend, that I was "not a business woman". Funny, huh?

God will take us where we need to go and give us what we need to get there.

Your business is an ever-evolving, dynamic, living creation. It is a gift from God and to be guarded carefully.

When I first started my business, I would have never defined myself using the term "entrepreneur". I really thought that term was reserved for men in high-rise buildings wearing fancy business suits. Little did I know that I would become an entrepreneur and then help other women to embrace their inner entrepreneur.

The Oxford Dictionary defines entrepreneur as "a person who undertakes or controls a business or enterprise and bears the risk of profit or loss."

Bobbi Brown, of Bobbi Brown Cosmetics, says it is "someone who has the vision to create something that others want."

Are you an entrepreneur?

Are you stumbling down the entrepreneur path like I did? I feel like I came in sideways, but when I look back, I now see God's hand all over my journey. As I reflect on my life and work I can see that I had an entrepreneurial mindset from a long time back. It is a blessing, and can be a curse. But we are what we are!

My mission is to help you, the Christian female on the entrepreneurial journey to be brave in ways that are FASTER, EASIER, and LEAVE LESS of a mess behind you!

I want to share my success and my failures so that you won't have to go through them. And yes, I have had quite a few of the failures along with the successes.

Let's take a look at a few official definitions now:

© 2010-2013 Diane Cunningham Companies LLC

What is an entrepreneur?
Who is an entrepreneur?

An **entrepreneur** is a person who exercises initiative by organizing a venture to take benefit of an opportunity and, as the decision maker, decides what, how, and how much of a good or service will be produced. He or she supplies risk capital as a risk taker, and monitors and controls the business' activities as a manager. The **entrepreneur** is usually a sole-proprietor, a partner, or the one who owns the majority of shares in an incorporated venture. According to the Czech-US economist Joseph Alois Schumpeter (1883-1950), entrepreneurs are not necessarily motivated by profit but regard it as a standard for measuring achievement or success. He discovered that they (1) greatly value self-reliance, (2) strive for distinction through excellence, (3) are highly optimistic (otherwise nothing would be undertaken), and (4) always favor challenges of medium risk (neither too easy, nor ruinous).

What is entrepreneurship?

It is defined by the BusinessDictionary.com as "Capacity and willingness to undertake conception, organization, and management of a productive venture with all attendant risks, while seeking profit as a reward".

They go on to say that the "Entrepreneurial spirit is characterized by innovation and risk-taking, and an essential component of a nation's ability to succeed in an ever changing and more competitive global marketplace."

We do live in a global world and it gets smaller day by day. This is changing how we do business and who we can do business with. God is all over this expansion of our territory. Remember the Prayer of Jabez: *Jabez cried out to the God of Israel, "Oh, that you would bless me and enlarge my territory! Let your hand be with me, and keep me from harm so that I will be free from pain." And God granted his request.* 1 Chronicles 4:10

What is innovation?

I love to create things and my mind gets me into trouble with all of the ideas that I can get brewing. This is innovation. It is defined as a "process by which an idea or invention is translated into a good or service for which people will pay. To be called an innovation, an idea must be replicable at an economical cost and must satisfy a specific need. **Innovation** involves deliberate application of information, imagination, and initiative in deriving greater or different value from resources, and encompasses all processes by which new ideas are generated and converted into useful products. In business, **innovation** results often from the application of a scientific or technical idea in decreasing the gap between the needs or expectations of the customers and the performance of a firm's products. In a social context, innovation is equally important in devising new collaborative methods such as alliance creation, joint venturing, flexible working hours, and in creating buyers' purchasing power through methods such as hire purchase."

Are you innovative? I have no doubt that you are. My hope is that this toolkit will help add more ideas and help you to clarify all areas of your business.

© 2010-2013 Diane Cunningham Companies LLC

The Two Types of Women

In my coaching practice I have found that there are two distinct types of women that seek my help, support, and expertise. Which type are you?

Woman #1 knows exactly what type of business she plans to launch.

My client Georgeanne knows that she wants to open a dog kennel and also provide dog training. When she came to me, she was working full time in human resources and we began to create a plan for her to leave her job.

2013 Success Story Update:

Georgeanne was able to quit her full time human resources job in January of 2012 and go full time with her dog training business. As of this writing, she has 10-12 dogs at any given time and her business is thriving.

Woman #2 has a huge list of potential businesses that she might want to launch.

She is frustrated, restless, and might even use the word "hate" if she is still at a job. She is really unclear and has no idea if she can pull it off.

My client Dena came to me as a referral from a counselor. Dena was so miserable at her job and had sought counseling for the depression that swept over her each weekend as she began to think about going back to work. She was willing to do whatever it took to NOT feel that way anymore. Let me just tell you.....she is not depressed anymore!

You might know exactly how your business will look. But if you do, you are very rare. The women that arrive on my virtual doorstep most often have a few pieces of the puzzle and then we take a look at it together. We sort it out, rearrange it, investigate it, clarify it, and then launch it.

Why do you need a toolkit?

We have been given a gift by God with the desire and the inspiration. We have a talent or a service. People come to us to get "THIS" thing. We are so used to IT that we often let IT go unnoticed. We think everyone can do IT. We think IT is no big deal.

We say "why would anyone ever pay for that?" I am here to tell you that your mind is about to shift and your eyes will be opened. People will purchase and invest in things for so many reasons.

They want to reduce a "pain" in their life. They want to increase the joy in their life. They want to gain more time or eliminate stress.

We need a toolkit that will help us to walk this path.

© 2010-2013 Diane Cunningham Companies LLC

This toolkit is full of 10 chapters worth of business basics from a non-business mind. This toolkit is how I put my business together piece by piece without knowing or understanding what I was doing.

My goal is to share with you as a colleague, a coach, and a consultant. I have been in your shoes a few times. I have started and restarted. I have fallen down and gotten back up. I have trusted God for resources so I could pay the bill that was almost overdue. I have read every book I could and attended as many trainings as time and money would allow. I have invested in myself and my God-given gifts.

This toolkit will be your "go-to" place. Use it and abuse it. Make it your own. God loves doodles and colored pens and highlighters. He loves for you to be YOU! Let this toolkit be a shining example of you. God allows us to evolve and He most definitely allows our inspired ideas and business ventures to evolve.

Please know that your thoughts will change. What you write in chapter one, might need to be updated by the time you get to chapter six. Thus is the nature of being an entrepreneur.

Why is now the right time for you?

Today is always the right time. Now is the best time. This is the perfect time for you to go "back-to-school" too. Or let me put it this way, "where will you be if you don't do this?" Will you be in the same place? Stuck? Frustrated?

Let me share a SECRET

Here is my secret. I call it ACT FAST NOW. I choose to take action. This is one of my best secrets and I am now giving it away. I have always unknowingly lived by this philosophy of taking action now. It is in my nature to want to get started. I want to make a move. Some might call it impatience. I call it urgency and purpose. I do my research, make wise choices and then take action. Seems simple enough, right? But I have watched many of my clients and colleagues NOT doing this and I now can see the difference. In fact, I recently talked to some colleagues that I know and love that I met 5 years ago. After talking to a few of them, I had to shake off my feelings of depression. Each of these talented women told me they were doing the exact same thing that they had been doing 4 years ago. They were not moving forward, they were not taking risks. By moving fast, I know that I will make some mistakes along the way. I have allowed myself that freedom. By taking fast action, I am actually inviting more mistakes. But I am also inviting more blessings and a lot more results. If I am going to make a mistake, I would rather make it this month than wait and talk and ponder and talk more and make the same mistake in 5 months.

What is a Breakthrough?

Why do we need a breakthrough?

What is holding you back?

Is it fear? Or lack of organization?

Are you unwilling to make needed changes?

A **breakthrough** is defined in these ways:

© 2010-2013 Diane Cunningham Companies LLC

1. **important discovery:** an important new discovery, especially in science, medicine, or technology, that has a dramatic and far-reaching effect
2. **removal of barrier to progress:** an event that causes or marks the breaking down of a barrier to progress
3. **penetration of enemy line:** an attacking army's advance through and beyond an enemy's line of defense

As Christian women entrepreneurs, we might need to step forward to find our breakthrough. You might have to be willing to let go of something to reach a breakthrough.

Are you willing?

Are you ready?

Is it time for your breakthrough?

3 Warnings about this toolkit!

Warning#1: The entrepreneurial process is not linear. Many things can be happening all at the same time as you go through this journey. It might not happen in the exact order of the modules. In fact, I know that it won't. Trust the flow of your own brain and God's divine timing. At any given time, you might be doing things from each of the 10 categories or topics. Be flexible and adaptable. This will be how you will live your life as an entrepreneur, so you might as well get used to it. There are no rules and concrete timelines other than the ones you create for yourself.

Warning #2: You might begin to experience what I lovingly call "Entrepreneurial A.D.D.". My brain can be in about 20 places at once, or so I think. I can get myself on a multi-tasking loop where really all I am doing is creating a mass of creative chaos. Be warned. I suggest you learn to write down all of your ideas but keep yourself from acting on ALL of them at once. Keep an IDEA section in your day planner or a journal. Many of these brilliant ideas need to be dumped in the garbage after more reflection.

Warning #3: There is a strong chance that you will enjoy my favorite...... "Entrepreneurial Insomnia". Your brain won't shut off. You are thinking of ideas in the middle of the night. You wake up with the "idea of the century". You begin sleeping with a notepad or journal next to the bed. I am warning you. ☺

I can't wait to go on this journey with you! Let me know how I can help.... And know that I am praying for you!

Use the templates as you go along and get a few BONUS business templates from me also! Just go to www.nacwe.org/ToolkitResources and use the coupon code: success

---

© 2010-2013 Diane Cunningham Companies LLC

10 Ways to use this Toolkit!

#1 is Learning: You might use this material to add to your skills and knowledge base as a female entrepreneur.

#2 is Focus: You might be here to clarify your brand or re-define your services.

#3 is Tools: You might use this toolkit just to get access to new coaching tools, templates, and handouts.

#4 is Inspiration: You might use this information to gather up some new inspiration for yourself as you continue making decisions about your next step.

#5 is Motivation: You might use this training to see how someone else has "done it", and then create your own way.

#6 is Challenge: You might use this material to add a little healthy challenge and competition to your life and get you moving.

#7 is Launch: You might use this training to prepare to launch your brand new business.

#8 is Profit: You might use this guide to add a new profit center or increase your fees.

#9 is Fun: You might use this training to have some fun!

#10 is Personal Growth: You might use the toolkit to add to your personal and professional development this year.

Templates and Questions

Each chapter includes a variety of worksheets, templates, and coaching questions.

In this section, I have included pages for you to use throughout the process. You might want extra copies of each. You can also get these in easy to use handouts by getting the Inspired Business Toolkit "Implementation Success Package".

Timing: Some of you will be going through the toolkit in 10 weeks, some faster, some slower. There is no right way, only the right way for you. You might read this book in a weekend and get started right away.

Team or Staff: : If you have a team or staff, you are also encouraged to use these materials with them.

Templates to be used throughout:

- Master Action Plan
- Reality Check
- Monthly Checklist
- In the next 4 months...
- Master Plan of Attack
- The Daily 10 Checklist
- Weekly Dream & Idea Space (in each chapter)
- Weekly Marketing Checklist (in each chapter)
- Weekly Review (in each chapter)

© 2010-2013 Diane Cunningham Companies LLC

Pre-Checklist

Have you completed the following?

- ☐   **Master Action Plan**
- ☐   The Reality Check
- ☐   Monthly Checklist
- ☐   In the next 4 months...
- ☐   Master Plan of Attack
- ☐   Weekly Dreaming and Ideas
- ☐   Weekly Marketing Checklist
- ☐   Weekly Review

Master Action Plan

By the time I finish the Inspired Business Toolkit, I want to have completed...

By 6 months from now, I want to have completed....

By one year from today, I want to have completed...

My BIG business goal for 3-5 years is...

© 2010-2013 Diane Cunningham Companies LLC

The Reality Check

Reality Check: What is the current status of your business?

Write both positive and negative self-evaluation.

Income	Expenses
Staff/Team	Clients/Customers
Website	Brand
Hours Spent Working	Marketing
Location	Systems/Organization

Monthly Checklist

© 2010-2013 Diane Cunningham Companies LLC

In the next 4 months....

Goals, Plans, Events, Launch, ideas, etc

Month #1	Month #2	Month #3	Month #4

Master Plan of Attack

Services/Products/Events

January					
February					
March					
April					
May					
June					
July					
August					
September					
October					
November					
December					

© 2010-2013 Diane Cunningham Companies LLC

The Daily 10 Checklist!

Each day, I choose to ask myself the following questions

Step #1:   Assessment
Where am I today?

Step #2:   Clarify
What do I need to clarify today?

Step #3:   Test
What do I need to test or try today?

Step #4:   Feedback
What feedback would help me to "breakthrough" today?

Step #5:   Accountability
Who do I need to be accountable to today?

Step #6:   Strategy
What is my strategic plan for today?

Step #7:   Truth
If I spoke the truth today, what would I say?

Step #8:   Networking
Where can I make some connections today?

Step #9:   Opportunities
What are my biggest opportunities today?

Step #10:   WOW! Women of great worth!
What is my unquestionable worth today?

Weekly Dream & Idea Space

© 2010-2013 Diane Cunningham Companies LLC

Weekly Marketing Checklist

Date	Networking Event, Article, Newsletter, etc

Weekly Review

What action(s) did I take during this week?

What were my wins or successes this week?

What were my challenges this week?

What have I learned about myself this week?

What is my focus for the upcoming week?

What progress have I made toward my goals? What has changed?

What three words would I use to describe this week?

© 2010-2013 Diane Cunningham Companies LLC

Chapter #1
Mission

© 2010-2013 Diane Cunningham Companies LLC

What is your mission?

We each have a WHY, a reason, a mission, a purpose. God has placed us here for a reason and He needs our gifts to be used.

What is your purpose? What is the purpose of your business?

Why do you do what you do as a female entrepreneur?

What is your WHY?

This mission or passion is the foundation of your business and your life. It is running as an undercurrent beneath the surface whether you are aware of it or not. Your business exists for a reason. It serves people. It offers a product or system. It might help to relieve pain or frustration. It offers solutions and strategies and makes the world easier.

Sometimes our mission feels so big, that we avoid it. It feels like it is too much for us. I wish I had a $100 for every time I thought to myself, "who am I to do that?". We don't see that we have been specifically chosen by God for a reason.

Due to the vast mission and our huge WHY, we might tend to be wary and possibly even avoid claiming our mission fully. We know what it FEELS like, but we can struggle with being vague in the FACTS. I know this very well as it is an area that I have to be mindful of. Many of us, started our business with "no business being in business". I know I started with hardly any business knowledge. It was an area that was not fun or easy for me. It becomes an easy area for us to avoid.

Well we will avoid no longer! Come with me as we discuss your mission, your purpose, and your passions. We will also find out how your strengths work together with your experience to make you an expert. We will then end this chapter by understanding the importance of your core values.

Let's get to work...

What is a mission statement?

According to Encarta, a **mission statement** is a formal document that states the objectives of a company or organization. We want your mission statement to be clear, concise, and easy to remember. Laurie Beth Jones, author of <u>Jesus CEO</u> even says we should know it so well that we could recite it if needed while a gun is being held to our head.

The BusinessDictionary.com says this about a **mission statement**: It is a written declaration of a firm's core purpose and focus which normally remain unchanged, whereas business strategies and practices may frequently be altered to adapt to the changing circumstances. Properly crafted mission statements (1) serve as filters to separate what is important from what is not, (2) clearly state which markets will be served and how, and (3) communicate a sense of intended direction to the entire organization. A mission is different from a vision in that the former is the cause and the latter is the effect; a mission is something to be accomplished whereas a vision is something to be pursued for that accomplishment.

I have seen mission statements in every shape and form. I have seen them in glass covered frames, in colored paper on a bulletin board in a small cubicle, in a spiral bound journal, and on a

© 2010-2013 Diane Cunningham Companies LLC

napkin from the coffee shop. The place it is written is not important, it is the writing of it.

In working with women in my coaching practice, I have enjoyed the privilege of helping many of them create their mission statement. I began my coaching career as a Certified Life Purpose Coach and thus walked along side women during their purpose process. What was interesting was that as they discovered their purpose, many of them felt the calling to change careers and/or start a business. In essence, the women I was attracting were women just like me. They wanted to do what they loved. This led to the evolution of my practice over the years as I added more business training so I could be prepared to help my clients.

By helping them, I was helping me. By helping you, I am helping me. I am living my mission.

I have rewritten my personal mission statement numerous times over the last few years as I learn, change, and grow. It is a dynamic living sentence.

My mission is to inspire women to dream big, catch on fire, and change the world.

So I have the great joy of living my mission throughout the day.

Let me show you some examples:

I am living my mission as I coach my clients or lead a group.

I am living my mission when I meet a friend for coffee.

I am living my mission when I post a quote on Facebook.

You get the picture. It fits and it is my foundation.

What is your mission?

How would we see evidence of it today in your life?

Creating a Mission Statement

If you DO have a written mission statement, I would love to give you a BIG hug and say "Congratulations!" I would love to hear your mission too, so I would ask you to tell me by emailing me at diane@dianecunningham.com.

If you DO NOT yet have a written mission statement, come with me on this journey. There are many roads that will lead you to your destination. Let me share with you the one I use with my clients both in one-on-one appointments, large group workshops, and tele-classes.

Recently I hosted a 4-week tele-class and 33 women enrolled, all of which were entrepreneurs and were working either part time or fulltime in their business. When I got to this exercise I asked the question, "who has a personal mission statement?" I expected to hear a few YES's. I was astonished when all 33 women said "No". So we got down to business right away. They were ready. We had done the pre-work. I told them we were going to do my 2-minute mission statement exercise.

What is the 2-minute mission statement?

This is a tool that I created "on-the-fly" when working with a client a few years ago. I did NOT want her to think too hard or mull this over for too long. I wanted her gut response and her heart answer. I grabbed the timer from my desk, which I often use to keep me on track as I work on a project.

© 2010-2013 Diane Cunningham Companies LLC

Here is what I said, "I am going to give you some blank paper and 2 minutes. I want you to write down My mission in life is...or My purpose in life is... Don't edit or censor, just write what comes to mind and we will rearrange it all later. It might come out in bullet points or sentences. I am not concerned with the format, just the content. I want you to get what is in your head and heart onto this piece of paper. Ready. Set. Go." So she did just what I said. We had so much to work with after she finished. We then crafted it into a rough draft sentence for her to investigate.

Why a ROUGH DRAFT?

Letting it be a rough draft seems to make all the difference. It gives us permission to play with it and not be so serious. This helps us as we move forward to get feedback on it, which I strongly encourage.

Now that we have a rough draft personal mission statement, we could then begin to work on the rough draft business mission statement with the same process. With entrepreneurs, it can often be hard for us to see the separation between who we are and what our business is. As I have said before, being an entrepreneur is like hanging your heart out on a shingle.

At this point, it is time to do what I call "percolate" on the mission. We let it settle and simmer. I want you to say it out loud and share it with your family and friends. I want you to make sure each word has the right nuance and evokes the correct feeling. I want this mission statement to make you happy and proud. I want you to be excited about your mission.

Here are some examples of mission statements:

C3 for Women is dedicated to supporting women business owners through monthly Success Events, the Synergy Group peer advisory program, networking and professional development opportunities, and the annual Celebrating Women in Business Luncheon.

Michelle Martin

My mission is to inspire women to pursue their passions while being present in their homes by creating financial freedom through network marketing. *Karen Palmer*

My mission statement says I give women permission and re-sources to discover and carry out their God-planned life purpose! My life purpose is to give 'hope' to women who think they have nothing to give, who have been beat down emotionally and have to look up to see bottom. Hopeful Heart Coaching endeavors to give women freedom from those pre-recorded tapes and permission to live in their strengths and giftings. *Rhoda Baty*

Mission, Purpose, and Passion

God has given each of us a unique mission and purpose. How can you use your mission to help define your business? We are women of many passions, both healthy and unhealthy. We each have a unique set of passions and this passion is what got you started with your business in the first place. This passion will keep you going too.

Real Women on Purpose

Dena is passionate about baking. The woman loves to bake cookies, cakes, pies, and her unique specialty "the brownie pop". She took action right away after she clarified her WHY. Fast forward

 © 2010-2013 Diane Cunningham Companies LLC

to now, and the result of our 3 months of coaching, is the birth of her company Dream Bakers.

Take a look at what Dena shares on her website:

Hi...my name is Dena Hoban and I am the CEO of Dream Bakers. Dream Bakers mission is to create special memories through unique and inspiring edible treats. My personal mission is to give generously to all those that God places in my path through listening, and celebrating the special moments of their lives. Jeremiah 29:11 "For I know the plans I have for you," declares the Lord, "plans to prosper you and not to harm you, plans to give you hope and a future."

Dream Bakers has been a passion of mine for practically my entire life. I started it because the passion has always been in my heart and for different reasons throughout my life that passion has been forced to be a small part of my heart when finally, truly letting God take control of my life, and connecting with the right people this passion has exploded in my heart and mind – it's so exciting I feel like I'm on fire!

Dena has the passion she needs to keep going!

Now I want you to meet Tammy Kniffin, the President and Founder of the Global Alliance of Special Needs Support (www. ga-sns.com).

Take a look at the mission that she has created:

The primary mission of GASNS is "connecting parents and professionals" in support of individuals with special needs. Our goal is to create a community where we provide information, support, resources, inspiration and connections for parents and others who have someone in their life with learning differences, different abilities or other issues that present unique challenges to everyday life. These may include ADHD, Autism Spectrum Disorders, Learning Disabilities, Down-Syndrome, or any number of other difficulties that impact your family.

Tammy says this: *I have dreamed of somehow serving other parents of special needs children for some time. I have the unique perspective of not only being the parent of two children with special needs, but also a special education teacher and a school counselor. I know that I can use these collective experiences to support and connect with other parents. It just took a while to find the way to accomplish this. So, although ideas and plans have been festering for a while, the culmination of all this officially launched June 29th 2010, as the Global Alliance of Special Needs Support.*

Tammy is using her experience, her passion, and her knowledge to live out her mission. It inspired her enough to launch her association, thus creating a ripple effect on the world. Great job Tammy!

Embracing your Strengths

According to the BusinessDictionary.com **strengths** are the capital, knowledge, skill, or other advantage that a firm has or can acquire over its competitors in meeting the needs of its customers.

What are your unique strengths that impact your business?

What is your unique area of brilliance?

What are you known for?

Your strengths are a big piece of the puzzle that we are putting together. They can also become your individual signature that is your leverage.

© 2010-2013 Diane Cunningham Companies LLC

So then you might be asking...what is this LEVERAGE?

What is your Leverage?

Leverage is the ability to influence a system, or an environment, in a way that multiplies the outcome of one's efforts without a corresponding increase in the consumption of resources. In other words, leverage is an advantageous-condition of having a relatively small amount of cost yield a relatively high level of returns. Thus, "doing a lot with a little."

Leverage can be:

- Time
- Connections
- Money
- Determination
- Intelligence
- Etc

What is your leverage?

How can you use your leverage to impact your business?

Me, an EXPERT?

It is said that anyone who is from out of town who comes to present a lecture, is considered an expert. Even Jesus had to leave his home town to gain the following and impact of his expertise.

An **expert** is somebody with a great deal of knowledge about, or skill, training, or experience in, a particular field or activity.

You are an expert. We all have areas of expertise that we think nothing about.

Let me give you an example from Tereson Dupuy, the founder of Fuzzibunz.com.

I started my business when I was only 28 years old after my son Eden who was suffering with chronic diaper rash needed a better solution for a diaper. Not being one to shy away from a challenge I sought to not only fix his rash when a "cloth diaper" option but to tackle all of the things I found unsatisfactory with both disposable AND cloth diapers. I knew I could do better than the square pieces of cloth that were out there. I am smart woman! After initially fixing the rash problem I quickly sought to make this a business – however I never imagined how big this business or this industry for that matter would grow. It is rare to NOW find a cloth diaper that does NOT have polar fleece incorporated into it somehow – I made that happen. I started sewing diapers in my home and now we manufacturer in an industrial facility and provide products globally to parents all over the world.

What are you an expert in and how can you use that?

What unique experiences have you had that make you stand out?

What are core values?

Core Values are operating philosophies or principles that guide an organization's internal conduct as well as its relationship with the external world. Core values are usually summarized in the mission statement or in the statement of core values

Let's take a look at an example to help us get started.

© 2010-2013 Diane Cunningham Companies LLC

Here are the **core values** from iBloom, founded by my friend and colleague Kelly Thorne Gore. You can find them at www. iBloom.us!

Mission: Inspire Women

1. to discover and live out their unique God-given life purpose
2. to live balanced, healthy, and thriving lives
3. to become passionate in their personal relationship with God

Core Values

Balance- As an organization and team we model what it means to live a balanced, healthy, and thriving life. First, is our relationship with Christ and personal growth (physical, emotional, spiritual). Second, is our family and friends. Third, is iBloom.

Servant Leadership- We lead by serving and investing in others. We treat everyone-no matter his or her position in life-as we would want to be treated. We lead by inspiring others to reach their fullest potential, often beyond what they dreamed possible.

Integrity- iBloom is an organization of integrity. We strive to do what is right, regardless of the cost or sacrifice. In every decision, we follow the principle in Matthew 7:12 – "So in everything, do to others what you would have them do to you"

Enthusiasm- Our enthusiasm and joy for life is contagious. Our enthusiasm encourages a positive attitude and provides inspiration as we work together to achieve our goals.

Value Others- We help others recognize their value in Christ. Our goal is to make everyone we come in contact with "feel important."

Quality- iBloom provides premier customer service, products, services, and events. We strive to remain culturally relevant in our mission of inspiring women.

Teamwork- The iBloom staff is a team. We are a group of people who collaborate and interact to reach the common goal of iBloom being successful. We need one another to reach our fullest potential as individuals and as an organization.

Generosity- iBloom is committed to giving back to the community and to organizations that further our mission of inspiring women. We tithe 10% of our time and resources.

What are your core values?

What are the core values of the company you are building?

Handouts, Worksheets, and Templates

- Mission Statement
- Passion and Purpose Quiz
- Strengths Assessment
- Core Values

© 2010-2013 Diane Cunningham Companies LLC

Mission Checklist

Have you completed the following?

- ☐ Personal Mission Statement
- ☐ Business Mission Statement
- ☐ Passion and Purpose Quiz
- ☐ List of your strengths (from Strengths Assessment)
- ☐ List of your areas of leverage (from Strengths Assessment)
- ☐ List of your areas of expertise (from Strengths Assessment)
- ☐ List of your core values
- ☐ Weekly Dreaming and Ideas
- ☐ Weekly Marketing Checklist
- ☐ Weekly Review

Mission Statement

Personal:

Business:

© 2010-2013 Diane Cunningham Companies LLC

Passion and Purpose Quiz

I am passionate about....

I love to be around people who are.....

I feel like I am making a difference when.....

I am the happiest and most fulfilled when....

Some of my best times are when....

My favorite hobbies/activities/ "fun things to do" are....

Strengths Assessment

I am especially good at:

I am not so good at:

Things I enjoy doing:

What is my LEVERAGE?

How am I an EXPERT? In what areas do I have a unique skill or knowledge?

© 2010-2013 Diane Cunningham Companies LLC

My Core Values are:

Choose your top 5-7:

Community

Nurturing

Innovation

Value

Diversity

Reliability

Trust

Positive outlook

Irreverence

Underpromise, overdeliver

Teamwork

Family

Competitiveness

Entertainment

Connection

Authenticity

Commitment

Disclosure

Fun

Performance

Simplicity

Comfort

The Golden Rule

Health

Responsiveness

Education

Pragmatism

Sense of urgency

People

Precision

Safety

Affordability

Integrity

Knowledge

Quality

Cleanliness

Fairness

Security

Honesty

Advanced technology

Growth

Customer focus

Creativity

 © 2010-2013 Diane Cunningham Companies LLC

Weekly Dream & Idea Space

Weekly Marketing Checklist

Date	Networking Event, Article, Newsletter, etc

© 2010-2013 Diane Cunningham Companies LLC

Weekly Review

What action(s) did I take during this week?

What were my wins or successes this week?

What were my challenges this week?

What have I learned about myself this week?

What is my focus for the upcoming week?

What progress have I made toward my goals? What has changed?

What three words would I use to describe this week?

© 2010-2013 Diane Cunningham Companies LLC

Chapter #2
People

© 2010-2013 Diane Cunningham Companies LLC

Who are your people?

May God Almighty bless you and make you fruitful and increase your numbers until you become a community of peoples. Genesis 28:3 (Today's New International Version)

We each have a group that is our unique group, our people. God has called each of us into a community to be used.

What group does your business serve?

Who is your ideal client?

Who are you meant to work with?

As you continue to define your business, it is crucial to decide on a niche. Now this is something that sounds easy but can be very challenging. We are so scared to leave anyone out. We are afraid that we are going to lose business. Often, we have no idea where our niche is or how to find it. And yet, if we don't define our niche, we will lose business. If fact, people will have no idea who we serve and what we provide.

What is a niche?

1. **suitable place for somebody:** a position or activity that particularly suits somebody's talents and personality or that somebody can make his or her own
2. **specialized market:** an area of the market specializing in one type of product or service

Your niche might be based on a combination of the following:

- Your life experiences
- Your education
- Your career history
- Your location
- Your purpose

Here are a few examples of Christian women working in their niche. Each is very different and as we do more research, we can see how and why the niche fits each of them perfectly.

Niche Example #1 is Stephanie Ecke, The Trauma Queen www.stephanieecke.com

Stephanie's Mission Statement: *I want to faithfully and passionately help people heal, restore and transform their lives on every level in order to become all that God created them to be.*

Stephanie Ecke is a Licensed Professional Counselor (LPC) and Licensed Chemical Dependency Counselor (LCDC). She has extensive trauma resolution training and uses mind/body techniques to help clients heal from trauma. While she works with a variety of clients, Stephanie specializes in trauma and addiction. She trained at The Meadows with Pia Mellody, a pioneer in the fields of codependency and addiction. She is committed to helping her clients find freedom from trauma and addiction, and celebrates their successes as they step into new, bright, hopeful futures.

Niche Example #2 is Dodie Robey who own Upscale Resale Consignment Boutique in Wichita Falls, Texas

Dodie Robey has always loved clothes and all the stuff that goes along with them. In 2002, she opened Upscale Resale to capture

© 2010-2013 Diane Cunningham Companies LLC

an untapped market…gals who normally wouldn't go to a resale shop. She decided that the only apparel she'd consign would be GENTLY worn and of FINE quality.

Dodie is a member of NARTS (National Association of Resale and Thrift Stores). She believes that whether you operate a retail store or a resale store, it should be done with professionalism and top notch customer service. She would love for you to come by and see what Upscale Resale has to offer..and don't forget to clean out your closet before you come. Dodie is ALWAYS looking for those quality pieces you don't wear anymore. Remember the rule of thumb…if you haven't worn it in the last 12 months, you probably won't.

Niche Example #3 is Camille Gaines from FinancialWoman.com

Financial Woman provides information and products to educate and inspire you to become empowered around your money and have the financial skills and security you want.

Camille Gaines's passion for investing began when she saw her father successfully time the purchase of municipal bonds in the early 1980's when interest rates on the bonds were as high as 20%, and municipal bonds were selling at deep discounts. Her father's theory was that "the last thing to go out would be the lights." He was right. Those same municipal bonds appreciated in value and paid tax free interest up to 20% over the next decade, allowing her father to take an early retirement and enhanced her parent's lifestyle.

These women each have very focused areas of expertise and are using their life experiences.

So what is your niche?

What is your niche?

What need are you filling?

Now that you have your purpose and know your area of expertise, this can help you find a place or position to claim as your niche. This is the group of people that God specifically needs you to work with. You are uniquely positioned to do this.

3 important facts about your niche:

1. It will change over the years

2. You will be able to work with other people too

3. Sometimes it is right in front of you and yet you can't see it

I posted this question in the private forum for members of NACWE and the following responses emerged:

Question: *How did narrowing your niche help you or increase your business?*

Lanel Taylor Truthfully my niche just kind of happened and I realized what it was after the fact. The groups I work with we always talk about the importance of defining your niche. Some struggle with this because they are so new in business that they need clients. For them, I encourage them to keep a running list of services/skills they enjoy and those they don't. For defining their client I encourage them to list traits they like and dislike so they can see who their ideal client is.

Rhoda Baty It helped me know what to give my time to.

 © 2010-2013 Diane Cunningham Companies LLC

Marlee D'Arco I stopped trying to make everyone happy. It was liberating. The truth is, I have a message, and a lot of people aren't going to like it. When I dropped caring about that, everything improved in my business. It's all about knowing who God has called you to serve and serving those people unabashedly.

Robin Hardy It increased my business because I became the expert to my target audience by focusing on them.

What is a target market?

A **target market** is a particular market segment at which a marketing campaign is focused.

Stephanie Ecke can target her marketing to men and women who have experienced a trauma. Dodie Robey would be seeking to market to upscale professional women in the surrounding area who love to shop. Camille Gains is looking for women who are ready to learn more about their financial future and empower them with the skills to take action.

What is niche marketing?

The BusinessDictionary.com says that **niche marketing** is concentrating all marketing efforts on a small but specific and well defined segment of the population. Niches do not 'exist' but are 'created' by identifying needs, wants and requirements that are being addressed poorly or not at all by other firms, and developing and delivering goods or services to satisfy them. As a strategy, niche marketing is aimed at being a big fish in a small pond instead of being a small fish in a big pond.

When you have a defined niche, your potential clients know exactly who you work with and how you can help them.

So, who is your ideal client?

Who do you really truly want to work with?

And just as important, who do you NOT want to work with?

Where is your tribe?

Seth Godin is the author of <u>Tribes: We Need You to Lead Us.</u> This book is just one of his twelve books that have been translated into more than thirty languages. Everyone has been a bestseller. He writes about the post-industrial revolution, the way ideas spread, marketing, quitting, leadership and most of all, changing everything.

In Tribes, he shares about the desire for all of us to join with a group or a community. We want to be lead. We want to be a part of a movement. We have the desire to connect.

Seth Godin says "A tribe is a group of people connected to one another, connected to a leader, and connected to an idea."

He also says that "tribes are about faith- about belief in an idea and in a community."

Where is your group? Where is your family?

This is one of the primary purposes of the **National Association of Christian Women Entrepreneurs** that I created and launched in early 2010. It is a group, or tribe, of like-minded

© 2010-2013 Diane Cunningham Companies LLC

women from all industries who are seeking connection, ideas, resources, and ongoing training. Before my launch, I had considered creating this group without the Christian focus. I am so glad that I narrowed my niche and defined more clearly who NACWE serves. It has been a crucial component of success. I am with my tribe. I know the language and the struggle. I am part of the journey. It was important to me, that I did not have to censor my language or meet everyone's needs. There is no way that I could.

When we are defining our niche, and finding our tribe, it takes courage and it takes time. Allow yourself to explore. Trust the process. Understand that you will be with some tribes forever and some tribes you will find are not a fit for you. (Note: We will discuss more on this in the mentoring chapter also)

What is Market Research?

Market Research is a component of marketing research whereby a specific market is identified and its size and other characteristics are measured. Used also as an alternative term for marketing research.

We want to gather up our research and see where our unique talents, gifts, and expertise fit with what our clients need.

Gather your information

A **survey** is a detailed study of a market or geographical area to gather data on attitudes, impressions, opinions, satisfaction level, etc., by polling a section of the population.

Here is a sample survey that I have used to gather information. I set it up and then posted the link on my facebook page and announced it in my email newsletter. There are many survey tools such as SurveyMonkey.com as well as a variety of others.

Sample Survey

Here are the 10 questions I included in my 2010 survey.

Survey Title: Female Entrepreneur Survey

Question: What do you love about being a female entrepreneur?

Question: What are your biggest challenges as a female entrepreneur?

Question: How do you network for your business?

Question: Have you been a part of a mastermind group? If so, how has that influenced your growth?

Question: Do you have a written mission statement for your business/company?

Question: What is your biggest area of self-doubt in your business/company?

Question: Do you engage in ongoing learning through workshops/reading/retreats?

Question: How do you set healthy boundaries around your work and your life?

Question: What is the proudest moment or moments you have experienced as a female entrepreneur?

Question: What do you do to celebrate your business success?

What kind of information do you need to gather from your people? What do you need to ask your tribe?

© 2010-2013 Diane Cunningham Companies LLC

What questions do you have for them?

You could offer a gift for each person that completes the survey or enter each of them into a drawing. Give them a reason to tell you the information. Make it appealing. It is going to help you in so many ways. You can do it virtually through email or have a quick survey in your store if you have a local business.

Allow the **voice of the customer** This is called VOC and it is the collective insight into customer needs, wants, perceptions, and preferences gained through direct and indirect questioning. These discoveries are translated into meaningful objectives that help in closing the gap between customer expectations and the firm's offerings.

What survey can you create?

We have to commit to a niche market in order to clarify who it is that we serve and how we can help them. We have to stop being "wishy-washy". God calls us to a certain group, for a certain time. I see it as my mission field. Allow Him to show you right where you need to be and with whom.

Handouts, Worksheets, and Templates

- My Ideal Client is..
- My Ideal Client is NOT...
- My Tribes
- Connections Quiz

People Checklist

Have you completed the following?

- ☐   My Ideal Client is...
- ☐   My Ideal Client is NOT...
- ☐   My Tribes
- ☐   Weekly Dreaming and Ideas
- ☐   Weekly Marketing Checklist
- ☐   Weekly Review

© 2010-2013 Diane Cunningham Companies LLC

My Ideal Client is...

My ideal client is between _____ and _____ age.

My ideal client has the following characteristics:

My ideal client belongs to these organizations:

My ideal client has the following pains and problems:

My ideal client attends these types of events in person:

My ideal client has these dreams and hopes:

My ideal client reads these books, magazines:

My ideal client loves these websites:

My ideal client is known to be committed to:

My Ideal Client is NOT...

My ideal client is NOT:

My ideal client is NOT:

My ideal client is NOT:

My ideal client is NOT:

What I love about my ideal client is:

When I am not working with my ideal clients, I feel:

Get your Ideal Client templates and the other 45 business building
tools now just by going here: www.nacwe.org/ToolkitResources
(the coupon code is success)

© 2010-2013 Diane Cunningham Companies LLC

My Tribes (sample)

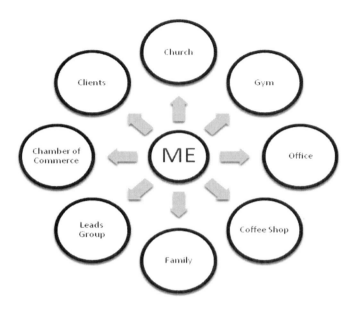

My tribes....

Weekly Dream & Idea Space

© 2010-2013 Diane Cunningham Companies LLC

Weekly Marketing Checklist

Date	Networking Event, Article, Newsletter, etc

Weekly Review

What action(s) did I take during this week?

What were my wins or successes this week?

What were my challenges this week?

What have I learned about myself this week?

What is my focus for the upcoming week?

What progress have I made toward my goals? What has changed?

What three words would I use to describe this week?

 © 2010-2013 Diane Cunningham Companies LLC

Chapter #3

Message

© 2010-2013 Diane Cunningham Companies LLC

What is your message?

"A brand is a living entity - and it is enriched or undermined cumulatively over time, the product of a thousand small gestures."
- Michael Eisner, CEO Disney

What is your unique message? Your brand? Your statement to the world?

The message of your company comes across in many ways. It is your brand. It covers a lot of territory including your company name, your website domain, your business structure, and your tagline.

Your message will evolve with you. Your image will change. We have to trust and release God to show us where to go as we continue with our business.

What is your brand? Well before we look at that, let's find out the definition of a brand. According to BusinessDictionary.com a **brand** is a unique design, sign, symbol, words, or a combination of these, employed in creating an image that identifies a product and differentiates it from its competitors. Over time, this image becomes associated with a level of credibility, quality, and satisfaction in the consumer's mind. Thus brands help harried consumers in crowded and complex marketplace, by standing for certain benefits and value. Legal name for a brand is trademark and, when it identifies or represents a firm, it is called a brand name.

A brand is a reflection of your identity. Let me give you an example from my journey. I have had my DianeCunningham.com website and domain name since 2004. It has gone through many updates, makeovers, do-overs and tweaks. My first website was built by my then husband in our living room with a "do-it-your-self" template. I then moved to the next level and hired my first website design company to create a real "grown-up" website for me. This was a step into unknown territory and like anything we do for the first time, it felt scary. The first time I saw the website they had created for me, I got tears in my eyes because it felt so impressive. I remember feeling like it was BIG, bigger than I was at the time. I felt like I was faking it...this is what we call "the imposter syndrome". Version #2 of my website was built around earth tones using brown, burnt orange, and some green. These colors were a reflection of who I was at the time and how I saw myself. This was my brand. Then as I learned and became bigger, we did a re-branding in 2006. This became version #3 of the website and it was full of green tones and fresh images. And now, we rebranded again for 2010 and all of my websites are in the red family. So DianeCunningham.com is on its version #4 now. The color is a big part of my brand. This is true of all companies and is true of yours too. What colors are you using?

Sometimes we outgrow our website (and/or brand) and it feels as if it does not reflect who we are any more. Watch for this feeling and listen for what you need to do. For me it feels like wearing an outfit that doesn't fit, or being overdue for a haircut. It gets more and more uncomfortable.

So what is branding?

Branding is the entire process involved in creating a unique name and image for a product (good or service) in the consumers'

© 2010-2013 Diane Cunningham Companies LLC

mind, through advertising campaigns with a consistent theme. Branding aims to establish a significant and differentiated presence in the market that attracts and retains loyal customers.

What is your brand?

Your brand can include the name, colors, programs, products, and/or services you offer. You might be your own brand, as I have been with my DianeCunningham.com journey or your brand might be a system or invention.

If you are involved in a franchise or a direct selling company, the brand might be already developed and waiting there for you. Here are 2 examples from members of the National Association of Christian Women Entrepreneurs. Lisa Lewis is an Independent Beauty Consultant with Mary Kay Cosmetics, a company we all know and love. She has a built-in brand and colors with name recognition. The other well known brand is Tupperware and we have Naomi Hartung who is a Legacy Executive Director. She has the benefits of being a part of a brand that has been around since 1946. Now that is some major impact and influence.

So what is your brand?

What is brand awareness?

Brand awareness is the extent to which a brand is recognized by potential customers, and is correctly associated with a particular product. Expressed usually as a percentage of target market, brand awareness is the primary goal of advertising in the early months or years of a product's introduction.

Some brands that we all know are Nike, Coke, Starbucks, Xerox, and Office Depot. Some people that have become a brand that we are all familiar with are Oprah, Michael Jordan, Larry King, Martha Stewart, and Rick Warren.

We want our customers and clients to know our brand and understand what we offer and who we serve. Much of our time in the early months is spent on creating this awareness.

Let's look at the name of your business and see how that relates.

What is the name of your business?

Choosing a name is a fun and challenging part of getting started. Some of you might have a name already. Some of you might need to change the name of your business to more fully reflect what you do now. I used to have the website LifePurposeCenter.com and had an office with that name too. That website and brand then morphed into the LifeInspirationCenter.com to reflect the changes in my niche. Then it folded into my bigger umbrella after I created NACWE.

What is the name of your business?

What does the name say about you and your company?

There are unique names that become a new word, such as Google and Twitter. Most of the time we want our name to showcase what we do or who we serve. We don't want to spend all of our time explaining our name.

Kristi Olsen is www.purposereleased.com

Her domain tells us what she does and how she can help.

Cindy Rushton has the www.writers-nook.com

© 2010-2013 Diane Cunningham Companies LLC

We know that this is a place for writers to go for information.

Karla Meachem hosts www.empoweringchristianwomen.com.

I understand the concept right away and know who she serves.

What about a website?

As much as possible, we want our website name to be the same as our business name. We want to make it as easy as possible for our customers to find us. Every business MUST have a website and use it. It has to be fresh and updated. It must help our prospects understand who we are and give them a "taste" of us. I was recently consulting with a church that had just created a beautiful new flyer to hand out about one of their services. As I looked over the flyer, I saw that the website was NOT listed on any part of the flyer. That is not how to do business, and yes a church is a business. I explained to the church that if I was to pick up that flyer at an office in town, the first thing I would do would be to look for the website before ever setting foot in the door. This is how the next generation of consumers do their research and make their buying decisions. I would also look for your church/ministry/ business on www.facebook.com in order to read your posts and to get a feel for who you are and what your company is about. I want to get to know you virtually.

So it is not a question of DO I get a website? It is how soon can I get a website online and start using it. You will start with getting a domain name or URL. I can get lost for hours on Godaddy.com which is where I purchase my domain names.

For some of you, this might be old news. You might have many URL's saved or being used out there on websites that are LIVE.

But I also know that many of the women I work with in coaching are doing this for the first time.

Here are the website basics according to Diane!

- Each domain is $11-$12 for a year
- You can purchase a domain long before you are ready to launch your website
- Always purchase your name, if it is available, such as DianeCunningham.com
- Check for availability of names of your products or services
- You can "re-direct" a domain from one place to another

Let me give you an example from my business. I have slowly added domains and let other domains expire over the last 5 years. At this writing, I have 35 domains. Many are redirected to other places. Each website/domain serves a different purpose or provides a home for a different company.

Diane Cunningham.com is now directed to my speaking page on the NACWE website.

InspiredWomenSucceed.com goes the site that showcases the book with that same title.

NACWE.org is the home for the National Association of Christian Women Entrepreneurs and includes an expansive membership area.

DearFemaleEntrepreneur.com is for my book of the same title.

InspiredBusinessToolkit.com is the sales site for this book.

You might be asking, "what does it mean to re-direct?". You can "point" a website to another website so it is still working for you. I have NACWEconnect.com pointed to NACWE.org.

© 2010-2013 Diane Cunningham Companies LLC

Business Structure

When beginning a business, you must decide what form of business entity to establish. Your form of business determines which income tax return form you have to file. The most common forms of business are the sole proprietorship, partnership, corporation, and S corporation. You might also consider a non-profit. A Limited Liability Company (LLC) is a relatively new business structure allowed by state statute. Legal and tax considerations enter into selecting a business structure.

This is a topic that is best discussed with help from your accountant and/or lawyer. It is important to make this decision with your spouse also. See www.irs.gov for more information.

It is also important that you fill out a DBA, Doing Business As form in your local city, and any other required documents. Each state and city is different, thus I am going to refer you to seek help in your own area.

You can get more information on all of this from your local Small Business Development Center which is a place that I have used over and over again. Go to www.sba.gov to find the closest center and make an appointment. The services are free and have helped me grow and learn at each phase of my business development.

I have also used www.Legalzoom.com when I was in the process of getting the TradeMark for the National Association of Christian Women Entrepreneurs. This is a fabulous program that I can highly recommend.

Do not be afraid to ask questions throughout this process as many of these terms are not what you are used to. Take the time you need to make a wise decision. This is one area that I suggest that you do not need to move fast. It took me 5 years to move from a Sole Proprietor to an LLC. I took the time I needed.

Tag Line or Slogan

What is your business tagline?

A tagline is a simple and catchy phrase accompanying a logo or brand, that encapsulates a product's appeal or the mission of a firm and makes it more memorable. And which (when used consistently over a long period), becomes an important component of its identification or image.

I posted this question in the private forum for members of NACWE and the following responses emerged:

Question: *what is your tagline or slogan?*

Lanel Taylor Custom fit solutions for all your business needs.

Rhoda Baty Living Responsively to God's Word

Robin Hardy Your Full Service Virtual Assistance Solution!

Summer Alexander Your Business. Your Vision. My Help.

Spend time brainstorming your catchy phrase or message. Remember that you tagline will change and evolve, just like your brand and your website. My tagline when I started was "Get Inspired with Me!". I used this on my email newsletters and even had it on the back of my car along with my company name.

My tagline has evolved and so will yours. Starting to get the idea?

© 2010-2013 Diane Cunningham Companies LLC

Have fun and tell your story. Share your message in all of these different ways. Be as clear as you can be. Make it easy for your clients to understand your service.

What about the messages that our clients or customers give back to us? How can we use those to build our brand? The best way is through their own words, or what we call testimonials.

What is a testimonial?

A testimonial is a written recommendation from a celebrity or satisfied customer affirming the performance, quality, and/or value of a product or service. Testimonials are one of the most potent tools of marketing.

It is important to get testimonials to use in your marketing. Allow your clients and customers to tell you why they love your work.

When you get an email that says what they love about your product or service, save it. I send those emails directly to my web designer to add to my website.

Even if today is your first day in business, it is not too early. Often we get the best message about what WE do, and how we serve from our customer. Capture those messages! Be sure to use the testimonial on your website and in your brochure. Ask for permission, of course. Allow your clients to tell their own story.

Crucial parts of the testimonial

- Name of client
- Photo, if possible
- Brief and focused
- Real examples (numbers, results, feelings)

Handouts, Worksheets, and Templates

- Who Am I?
- Business Names Business Names/Domains
- Taglines to Try
- Weekly Dreaming and Ideas
- Weekly Marketing Checklist
- Weekly Review

Go to www.nacwe.org/ToolkitResources to get your own set
of the 47 templates by using the coupon code: success

© 2010-2013 Diane Cunningham Companies LLC

Message Checklist

Have you completed the following?

☐   Who Am I? Exercise

☐   Business Names/Domains

☐   Taglines to Try

☐   Weekly Dreaming and Ideas

☐   Weekly Marketing Checklist

☐   Weekly Review

Who am I? Exercise

This revealing exercise can help you as you continue to build your message and your brand. We want to have people tell us how they would describe us or our business using just 3 words. Send an email to at least 10 people, more if possible, and explain that you need their honest help and feedback.

- Ask them to email you back the 3 words they would use to describe you
- Ask them to email you back with the 3 words they would use to describe your business or what you do

You will be amazed at the results from this both personally and professionally. I suggest sending the email as a BCC and to people who you have known for years and people that you have just met. Get a wide variety of answers.

Names	Words

© 2010-2013 Diane Cunningham Companies LLC

Business Names/Domains

Business Name	Possible Domains
Example: *National Association of Christian Women Entrepreneurs*	*Nacwe.com* *Nationalassociationofchristianwomenentrepreneurs.com* *Nacwe-connect.com*

Tag Lines to Try

- [ ] _____
- [ ] _____
- [ ] _____
- [ ] _____
- [ ] _____
- [ ] _____
- [ ] _____
- [ ] _____
- [ ] _____
- [ ] _____
- [ ] _____
- [ ] _____
- [ ] _____
- [ ] _____
- [ ] _____

© 2010-2013 Diane Cunningham Companies LLC

Weekly Dream & Idea Space

Weekly Marketing Checklist

Date	Networking Event, Article, Newsletter, etc

© 2010-2013 Diane Cunningham Companies LLC

Weekly Review

What action(s) did I take during this week?

What were my wins or successes this week?

What were my challenges this week?

What have I learned about myself this week?

What is my focus for the upcoming week?

What progress have I made toward my goals? What has changed?

What three words would I use to describe this week?

© 2010-2013 Diane Cunningham Companies LLC

Chapter #4
Services

© 2010-2013 Diane Cunningham Companies LLC

What are your services?

No matter what your product is, you are ultimately in the education business. Your customers need to be constantly educated about the many advantages of doing business with you, trained to use your products more effectively, and taught how to make never-ending improvement in their lives. –Robert G Allen

What are the services that you will be providing?

What business model will you use?

How will you go about launching?

Do you offer a service or a product or a combination of both?

The services you offer will help your business to be easily understood by the customer. We do have to provide education for our clients and potential clients because no matter how many times we tell them what we offer, they still might not fully comprehend. Often it is much easier for our clients to look at a menu with only 3 choices versus 30 choices. As women with many inspired ideas, we can get carried away with the options we want to provide. Do yourself and your client a favor and make it very simple.

What are services?

Services are intangible products that are not goods (tangible products), such as accounting, banking, cleaning, consultancy, education, insurance, know how, medical treatment, transportation. Sometimes services are difficult to identify because they are closely associated with a good; such as the combination of a diagnosis with the administration of a medicine. No transfer of possession or ownership takes place when services are sold, and they (1) cannot be stored or transported, (2) are instantly perishable, and (3) come into existence at the time they are bought and consumed.

When you are selling a service, it can often feel like you are selling time or selling "air". In reality, you are selling your knowledge and your expertise. You are selling intellectual property.

What is Intellectual Property?

Intellectual Property (IP) is a term referring to a number of distinct types of creations of the mind for which property rights are recognized--and the corresponding fields of law. Under intellectual property law, owners are granted certain exclusive rights to a variety of intangible assets, such as musical, literary, and artistic works; discoveries and inventions; and words, phrases, symbols, and designs. Common types of intellectual property include copyrights, trademarks, patents, industrial design rights and trade secrets in some jurisdictions.

Although many of the legal principles governing intellectual property have evolved over centuries, it was not until the 19th century that the term intellectual property began to be used, and not until the late 20th century that it became commonplace in the United States.

This book/toolkit/manual is full of intellectual property. I have secured the trademark for the National Association of Christian Women Entrepreneurs™. What do you need to TradeMark?

 © 2010-2013 Diane Cunningham Companies LLC

What is your menu of services?

You might have one service or many services to choose from. Each business is different and can often benefit from thinking "outside the box" when considering what services to offer.

Tandi Brayson-Foster is the founder of The Joy Love Club which offers one service, a women's group. There are 4 groups that are currently in process that are offered at different times. www.thejoyloveclub.com

Sally Gray owns Welcome To Texoma, which offers one service which is to welcome newcomers to the local area. Her clients are the business owners that want to be included in her welcome basket. The other client for her is the new person who moves to town. www.welcometotexoma.com

Linda Neal provides accounting services with her business Numbers Count. Under this umbrella, she might offer a variety of options that will fit different types of clients.

What are your products?
What are your product lines?

My business includes both products and services. I have been adding more products each year. These would be called information products.

Information Products include all books, reports etc. In the Internet context, the term refers to electronically deliverable, knowledge-based products. Information products are also referred to as "digital goods" and "knowledge-based goods".

If it delivers knowledge and you can e-mail it to the customer or offer it as a downloadable file, then it qualifies as an information product. Most often these are automated so the client gets the information right away in their email inbox.

Information Products can be:

Free Report

- Checklist
- E-book
- Audio Message
- Tutorials

Look at some of my Information Products on these websites:

Quick Start Guide at www.nacwe.org/freetraining

Inspired Business Video Vault www.nacwe.org/videovault

What could you provide for you clients or customers that be a great information product? How can you create something once that can be used over and over again?

Take a look at our NACWE success store with products that are ready to help you move forward at your own pace: nacwe.org/nacwe-store/

A product line is:

1. **company's whole range of products:** the whole range of products marketed by a company
2. **company's group of related products:** a group of related products marketed by the same company that differ only in size or style

© 2010-2013 Diane Cunningham Companies LLC

Example of Product Lines

Coaching	Speaking	Products	Training
Go BIG group 1:1 Clients	Business Women's Symposium	Dear Female book Inspiration Blueprint Dreams and Goals ebook	Life Inspiration Coach

What is product development?

Product Development is the creation of products with new or different characteristics that offer new or additional benefits to the customer. It may involve modification of an existing product or its presentation, or formulation of an entirely new product that satisfies a newly defined customer want or market niche.

What is a product launch?

A **product launch** is the debut of a product into the market. The product launch signifies the point at which consumers first have access to a new product.

Before you launch a new product, there is a great deal of marketing that needs to happen so your clients are ready. This is often called Pre-Launch and it can be used to generate a "buzz" about your upcoming announcement or demonstration or grand opening.

As you prepare for your launch, you will want to consider the financial impact. How much money will it cost to get started? How much time will it take? What are the benefits? What will happen if I don't make this move or take this next step?

What is your break-even point?

It is important to pay attention to your break-even point for your business as a whole and each product line.   This is a key factor in deciding if you will go down a certain path or not.

Just to use a simple example with some easy numbers. If you have invested $1,000 to get started in your business, how soon will you make that $1,000 back and begin to make a profit?

What is ROI?

ROI is Return on Investment which is an important part to discover as you prepare for launch.

ROI is the percentage income from investment: profit from an investment as a percentage of the amount invested.

What is a business model?

A **business model** describes the rationale of how an organization creates, delivers, and captures value - economic, social, or other forms of value. The process of business model design is part of business strategy.

In theory and practice the term business model is used for a broad range of informal and formal descriptions to represent core aspects of a business, including purpose, offerings, strategies, infrastructure, organizational structures, trading practices, and

© 2010-2013 Diane Cunningham Companies LLC

operational processes and policies.

It views the business as a system and answers the question, "How are we going to make money to survive and grow?"

A few examples of different types of business Models are:

Direct Sales Model

Send Out Cards uses the direct sales model and Kathy Hadziba-jric is an independent consultant.

Franchise

Pam Russell owns a franchise with Proforma that showcases marketing products. www.proforma.com/specialtymarketing

Subscription Business Model

The National Association of Christian Women Entrepreneurs is built using a subscription or membership based business model. www.nacwe.org

There is a lot to consider as you look at your current products and services. Think about these questions and use them as you move forward.

What can you automate?

What type of team do you need?

Will this make things easier or more complicated for your clients?

How can you use technology?

Who are your competitors?

Are you underpriced or overpriced?

What is a SWOT?

A SWOT is a situation analysis in which internal strengths and weaknesses of an organization, and external opportunities and threats faced by it are closely examined to chart a strategy.

What are strengths and weaknesses?

Positive or negative aspects of the external and internal environments that are under the direct control of a firm or a decision maker.

What are opportunities and threats?

Agents, factors, or forces in an organization's external environment that are out of its control, and can directly or indirectly affect is chances of success or failure.

The SWOT is an amazing tool that I was so happy to find a few years ago. It is useful is so many situations and can be used for much more than just your business. Try using the SWOT with your family and volunteer activities and see what happens.

Don't forget to pray over your product lines and listen for answers. Often God wants to take us in a different direction that we first can see.

Handouts, Worksheets, and Templates

- Product Lines
- Product Launch
- SWOT

 © 2010-2013 Diane Cunningham Companies LLC

Services Checklist

Have you completed the following?

- ☐   Product Lines
- ☐   Product Launch
- ☐   SWOT
- ☐   Weekly Dreaming and Ideas
- ☐   Weekly Marketing Checklist
- ☐   Weekly Review

Product Lines

Product #1	Product #2	Product #3	Product #4	Product #5	Product #6

© 2010-2013 Diane Cunningham Companies LLC

Launch Plan

Product or Service to be launched:

What will it do? What is the Big Promise?

Name of Program:

How does it relate to my other products/programs/ services?

Cost of Product:

What is the break-even point?

Is it relevant and timely? Why now?

Does it excite me and give me energy?

Which clients do I know need this?

How can I build excitement?

- ☐   Free Tele-Class or Seminar
- ☐   Free Report
- ☐   Open House
- ☐   Early Bird Sale
- ☐   Extra bonus (product, group, service, coupon)

What else do I need to do?

SWOT Analysis

Situation analysis in which internal strengths and weaknesses of an organization,

and external opportunities and threats faced by it are closely examined to chart a strategy.

Strengths	Weaknesses
Opportunities	Threats

© 2010-2013 Diane Cunningham Companies LLC

Weekly Dream & Idea Space

Weekly Marketing Checklist

Date	Networking Event, Article, Newsletter, etc

© 2010-2013 Diane Cunningham Companies LLC

Weekly Review

What action(s) did I take during this week?

What were my wins or successes this week?

What were my challenges this week?

What have I learned about myself this week?

What is my focus for the upcoming week?

What progress have I made toward my goals? What has changed?

What three words would I use to describe this week?

© 2010-2013 Diane Cunningham Companies LLC

Chapter #5
Marketing

© 2010-2013 Diane Cunningham Companies LLC

What is marketing?

And let us not grow weary of doing good, for in due season we will reap, if we do not give up. Galatians 6:9 ESV

What do you need to do to get the word out?

How will your customers find out about you?

What is holding you back?

Let's go plant some seeds. I know that marketing is about planting seeds. I also know that you might think of marketing as a "bad word"! Please keep an open mind as we move through this module together. I love marketing and found out along the way that I was actually quite good at it. You might surprise yourself!

The BusinessDictionary.com tells us that **marketing** is the management process through which goods and services move from concept to the customer. As a philosophy, it is based on thinking about the business in terms of customer needs and their satisfaction.

As a practice, it consists in coordination of four elements called the 4P's:

Product: identification, selection, and development of a product

Price: determination of its price

Place: selection of a distribution channel to reach the customer's place

Promotion: development and implementation of a promotional strategy

I know that you might be scared of the word "marketing" and that you do NOT want to be a sales person. I have heard that so many times over the years, from so many women. You are not alone. But I want to challenge your thinking on this, and offer a mindset shift for you to consider. (We will be covering a lot of mindset shifts in the next chapter) I do think that as Christian women we have even more to overcome in this area. We mistakenly believe that we are not meant to be paid to use our gifts and talents. We often get caught in the guilt factor and end up serving for FREE. There is a unique challenge for us as many people in our lives want us to volunteer our time. I am completely supportive of volunteering and the fact that it is another non-negotiable. But that does not mean that it is OK to be undervalued, underpaid, and become what is called an "under-earner".

What is the Know-Like-Trust Factor?

People want to do business with people that they know, like, and trust. This is called the Know-Like-Trust factor. People buy based on emotional connection, hunger, or pain. People want to do business with other people that they feel know and understand them. They want to feel a connection. We want to know that we can trust the person we are handing our money to and spending our time with.

We want to alleviate the pain we are in, which could mean:

- Going to the dentist to get a broken tooth fixed
- That awful noise on the car
- A house that never cleans itself
- The dog that need a good grooming

© 2010-2013 Diane Cunningham Companies LLC

You get the picture. We are all out networking and connecting even when we are just living our regular life. You DO NOT ever have to step foot in a networking event, and yet you are still networking daily.

But, as a female entrepreneur, it is your job to make your business a name that is known. It is your job to be "out and about" alleviating the pain that your business helps with.

We have to market ourselves. We need to go out there and get connected at networking events. Or we even need to be brave enough to create our own if there is a group that needs to be created in your area. Why not you? Why not now?

Marketing Mindset

Here is the shift: You market every day, whether you think you do or not. Let me show you how we "market" for others without even thinking about it. When I tell you about a new restaurant that I love or you tell me about the new shoe store you found over the weekend. That is "word-of-mouth" marketing, which is the best kind. So my wise advice is to "get over it" and trust that you are going to learn how to market. The difference is that you are going to learn how to market yourself, your brand, and your company/product instead of marketing for someone else.

Marketing is a non-negotiable of having a business or staying in business. If you don't market, you better be doing a lot more than just praying because you are going to need some extra help. The way I see it, God has given me a business. It is how He wants me to be used for His kingdom. So why would I NOT tell people about it? That would make no sense and would be dishonoring to God. It would be a waste of the gifts He has given me. I do not want to waste this valuable and unique gift from my Father.

My job is to be "out and about" for God. I call this the "go, do, and be seen" principle and you will hear more about it later in this chapter.

Lets cover some basics before we get into the HOW part of what you are going to be doing. For everything in life there is time and a season. The same is true for marketing. Let's look at the marketing cycle.

A **marketing cycle** is based on your industry and the yearly calendar. If you are selling school supplies, you would base your marketing calendar on the school year. Every industry needs to plan ahead with a yearly marketing calendar that can help you see what you need to do now to be ready for later. This is really about having time for strategic thinking.

What is Strategic Thinking or Strategic Planning?

Strategic planning is a systematic process of envisioning a desired future, and translating this vision into broadly defined goals or objectives and a sequence of steps to achieve them. In contrast to long-term planning (which begins with the current status and lays down a path to meet estimated future needs), strategic planning begins with the desired-end and works backward to the current status. At every stage of long-range planning the planner asks, "What must be done here to reach the next (higher) stage?" At every stage of strategic-planning the planner asks, "What must be done at the previous (lower) stage to reach here?"

Strategic planning helps us to look at the wider picture and prepare in advance. The challenge comes as we get busy with more clients and customers. As we get busier with our business, we lose sight of the long term strategic plan. We are so busy build-

 © 2010-2013 Diane Cunningham Companies LLC

ing the business and working in all of the roles (CEO, marketing director, visionary, accountant, and janitor) that we can lose sight of the bigger picture. Often we are trying to prepare for the presentation tomorrow or the sale that starts next week. We can easily get lost in the current day or week, and forget to look out farther on the calendar. I have been guilty of this so many times over the years. For me, it is often related to an event where I will need additional business cards, flyers, or post cards and not ordering early enough. You might take action now, to block off time each week on your calendar that is simply called strategic planning. This way you will know that it will get done and you will not be scrambling around at the last minute to get the supplies you need.

What is the difference between marketing and networking?

There can be some confusion over these two words so let me help you to understand through some definitions and some examples. They are not the same but they are similar. We might call them sisters! In this chapter we will be talking about both.

Marketing is publicizing a service or product with the intent of closing a sale.

Networking is the art of making acquaintances and sharing information about yourself, your business, or your product. Its purpose is to build relationships that offer a mutual opportunity for both parties to prosper.

Thus, a business networking group may agree to meet weekly or monthly with the purpose of exchanging business leads and referrals with fellow members. To complement this activity, members often meet outside this circle, on their own time, and build their own "one-to-one" relationship with the fellow member.

For example, if I put up a flyer at my local coffee shop about my event, that is marketing. When I attend my weekly leads group through the local Chamber of Commerce, that is networking. I might hand out my flyer while I am there, so then I would be doing both.

Business networking can be conducted in a local business community, or on a larger scale via the Internet. Business networking websites have grown over recent years due to the Internet's ability to connect people from all over the world. Truly the social media sites have changes the way we do business. We must think about how we are networking both at "live" and "virtual" events.

Facilitated networking is when you create a group of acquaintances and associates that are willing to actively share leads and connections. The group is committed to keeping it active through regular communication for mutual benefit. Networking is based on the question "How can I help?" and not with "What can I get?".

Let me tell you a story from 2005 when I attended my first "real" networking event in San Antonio, Texas. I had just started my business which at the time was called Running Life Coach. Now as a woman, I had often attended luncheons, retreats, and women's events. This felt different. This event was at the Dominion Country Club, in the area of town where the Spurs basketball players live, along with other celebrities such as the writer and preacher Max Lucado. I felt impressed just driving into the parking lot. I was a guest of a man who was very well connected and called himself "The Master Networker". I wore my new business suit with black slacks and a lovely coral shade jacket. I really felt pretty snazzy but was very nervous walking in with my business cards. So I just said a quick prayer in my car before going in, not knowing what to expect.

© 2010-2013 Diane Cunningham Companies LLC

Upon entering, I felt totally and completely out of my league. I had never seen so many men in business suits in my entire life. And the women....WOW! They were each dressed much better than I was and appeared so successful. But what struck me, after getting the chance to talk to the group at my table, was that these people were just like me. Each had a business, but they were regular people too. I did just fine at connecting at my table. In fact, I would say I did better than most at having conversational skills and including others into the discussion. I realized that I could really get into this "networking" thing.

As I left the lunch and got into my car, the image that I kept seeing had much more depth. I realized that all of these grown-ups in their fancy clothes were no different than a group of pimply faced kids at the junior high dance. We all just wear more expensive clothes now and have less acne. Each person just wants to be loved and accepted. We all want to be successful, or appear that way. Each person at the event had their "game face" on and were doing the best that they could today with their life and their business. They all appeared wildly successful to me, but as I began to get to know these people, I found out the stories behind the image. Not all were that successful, and in fact some were on the brink of closing down their business. Many had marriages in turmoil and children that were in the midst of crisis. I had my "A-Ha" moment when I recognized that networking was about regular people, who just happen to have a business. This was a lesson that I needed to learn. Growing up in a family of teachers, who did not network, I had no concept of networking or marketing at the time.

This also taught me a powerful lesson about people that helps us when we are out planting our seeds (networking). Remember to always look for the story, under the story. Everyone is dealing with a sick child, an aging parent, a financial challenge, or a life altering decision. Everyone has a story to tell.

I continued attending a variety of networking events in San Antonio while I lived there, working on getting my name known, making decisions with my limited budget about where it was best to spend my time and money for the most impact. In a city of one million people, you can imagine the immense number of networking opportunities daily on all sides of town and for every type of group you could imagine. I looked at it as if I was dating, and each event/group got one chance with me, or "one date". This is a "mindset" trick that we will discuss more in the next chapter.

As I evolved, I learned how to be a better networker. So when we moved from San Antonio to the much smaller town of Wichita Falls, Texas, I was prepared and had a networking game plan in place before we even arrived. Wichita Falls has a population of approximately 100,000 people, which felt like a relief for me. It was much easier to get around with no traffic to speak of and easy access to local groups. I had done my research on local networking groups and women's clubs. I was ready to go and I got busy the month after we moved into the house.

This is where you might remember my secret to ACT FAST NOW. You will see what I mean with this timeline. We moved into our house on August 21st, 2006 and by the end of October I had done the following:

- Rented an office, moved in, and had a grand opening
- Joined the local Chamber of Commerce and began attending leads groups
- Joined Toastmasters
- Joined Business and Professional Women's BPW Club
- Got connected at a church

 © 2010-2013 Diane Cunningham Companies LLC

By November of 2006, I had started my own networking group at a local women's tea house and had our first few meetings. This group is still going on 7 years later with no dues, no fees, just women helping and supporting other women.

Look at what Rene Owens, a teacher and a Piggies and Paws artist just said about this group on my facebook page this week. "Thanks for letting me speak at your Networking Luncheon in August! I have had 3 galleries booked off of the connections made there. I want to say a big thank you to Dena Hoban for sharing my card at work. One of the ladies she works with told her daughter about it and she booked a gallery. Networking works!!! THANKS!!!!"

By January, I had been featured in an article about me in the local newspaper and spoken at a few local venues. I was on my way!

I realized along the way, that I LOVE NETWORKING!

I love to show up! I hate to miss out and I certainly don't want to miss any fun. It lights my fire to meet new people and find out about interesting opportunities. I love hearing new speakers and learning from each person that I meet. I find people incredible fascinating and I truly go into each event with the hope of a new friend, not making a sale or a deal.

As women, we are natural networkers on a daily basis. We connect, we gather, we exchange information (from a great local bakery, to where to get a haircut, to a website designer), and we network unofficially for each other constantly. We connect at the coffee shop, over lunch, at the garage sale, and even in the bathroom! We know how to show up for each other and with each other. We know how to network and we certainly know how to market.

But it would be much easier if we had a checklist or a recipe to follow, don't you think? What if we had a marketing plan?

What is a marketing plan?

According to the BusinessDictionary.com, a **marketing plan** is a written document that details the necessary actions to achieve one or more marketing objectives. It can be for a product or service, a brand, or a product line. Marketing plans cover between one and five years. A marketing plan may be part of an overall business plan. Solid marketing strategy is the foundation of a well-written marketing plan. While a marketing plan contains a list of actions, a marketing plan without a sound strategic foundation is of little use.

That sounds great, but I would like to offer you my version of a marketing plan. Sometimes we just need a plan for the next few months, or even the next 30 days. We want to try some new behaviors and cannot even fathom what we might need to be doing a year from now. Thus I have created the One Page Marketing Plan for you.

What is the One Page Marketing Plan?

The **One Page Marketing Plan** is a simple tool to help you focus on the current month or the next 30 days. You will want to keep it next to your monthly planning calendar and decide when you will complete each item that you choose. Make a goal and decide on your commitment. (See the example at the end of this chapter)

Be willing to try something new as you move out of your comfort zone. It is hard to know what will work best for you until you get

© 2010-2013 Diane Cunningham Companies LLC

comfortable with something. I caution you to NOT try everything at once. That will just lead you to feeling overwhelmed.

Decide on the "bottom line" marketing plan that could include 3 levels of marketing options.

Level #1 is the very basics that you commit to doing each and every month. This could be your e-newsletter and your social media.

Level #2 is the middle level that you might add as your income increases or for a special occasion or event. This could be the level #1 choices and some postcards or flyers.

Level #3 is the highest level that you might add when you have reached a certain income goal or gained a new ongoing contract. This could be both of level #1 and #2 and adding a TV advertisement or buying pay per click marketing on a site that you know your customers will be visiting.

What is Lead Generation?

Lead generation is a marketing term that refers to the creation or *generation* of prospective consumer interest or inquiry into a business' products or services.

Leads can be generated for a variety of purposes - list building, e-newsletter list acquisition or for winning customers. Lead generation is generally generated through search engines, direct mail, email, or telephone.

Let me take you on a virtual tour of the things I use for lead generation. Many of these have only recently been added. Others are what I have been using for years. I will give you the behind the scenes information as we move through them.

I will be showing you:

- Auto-responders
- Freebies
- Events
- Social Media
- Joint Ventures
- Books
- Affiliates
- YouTube
- BlogTalkRadio
- Mini-sites
- Blogs
- Newsletters or ezines

Keep in mind that you are going to be choosing a few things to try, not everything all at once.

What is an Auto-responder?

An **autoresponder** is a program which automatically generates a response when it receives information. The classic use of auto-responders is in email management, but these programs can also be found on websites. This type of program can be a very useful and powerful tool for everything from internet marketing to managing admissions to a university. Many people have encountered some version of the autoresponder at some point in their lives.

Here is a 30 day autoresponder sign-up form and website that I created in 2010 called Be Brave Today. When a client signs up, they will get an email from me each day for 30 days. I include a message, a few links, and a quote. This is an example of a FREE

© 2010-2013 Diane Cunningham Companies LLC

auto-responder. It would also be considered a FREEBIE or an Opt-In. Go to www.bebravetoday.com to see!

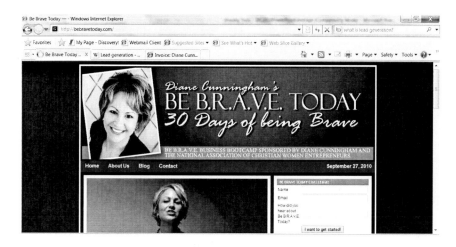

This is an example of a PAID auto-responder series that I created in 2010 called 90 Days to Marketing Success. It uses a series of emails that include video links. This program is $77 and the client gets a video training from me every 3 days that is 3-5 minutes long. I also turned this into a DVD product. Go to www.90daystomarketingsuccess.com to see!

NOTE: For each of the screen shots in this workbook, I encourage you to go take a look at the website for yourself to see it in action!!

What is a Freebie?

A **freebie** is a promotional gift or something given or obtained free of charge. It can be something such as a free report or an E-book. It is also called an Opt-In because you want people to opt-in to get information from you.

You will want to keep your freebie updated and change it as you see if it is working. Try new things. Find what gets people to want to opt-in.

We have used a free report "19 Inspired Ideas for Marketing", sent 3 bookmarks sent by mail, had a 38 page ebook, and offered a 7 day video ecourse. www.nacwe.org/freetraining

It is important to have an Opt-in Box at the top of your website in the header or on the side bar. Make it easy to find.

See the Opt-In box below on the right side of the screen.

© 2010-2013 Diane Cunningham Companies LLC

You could offer any of the following:

- Free Report
- Checklist
- Ebook
- Quiz
- Bookmarks
- Audio download

We also offer a FREE webinar each month as a Freebie and another way to get people to join us. It is called the Inspired Business Cafe and it happens on the first Wednesday of every month.

Join us for the Inspired Business Café each month on the 1st Wednesday. Go here to get registered for this fun and free training and networking experience! www.nacwe.org/cafe

---

What about Events for lead generation?

Events are a great way to connect with leads and build your tribe of followers and fans.   This can include both live and virtual events.

- Pre-View Calls
- Open House at a local office
- Speaking at a Virtual Conference
- Book Signing
- Facebook.com Party

This is the invitation for the facebook party I hosted for Christian Women Entrepreneurs. You can see on the left that we had 61 women who planned to attend. We ended up with 50 there. Not bad for hosting a party online with only a one-week notice. A facebook party is something that happens on your facebook fan page to promote growth and build a buzz.

Here is the invitation for the Book Signing for Inspired Women Succeed book launch in my local area:

© 2010-2013 Diane Cunningham Companies LLC

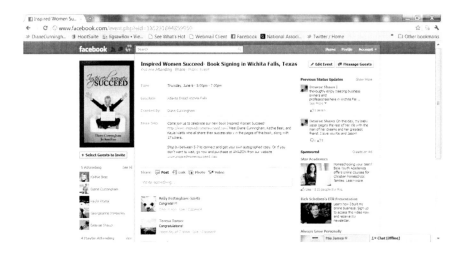

This is an event that I was a part of in 2011 hosted by one of the members of NACWE. Be willing to speak to other groups as a part of your marketing strategy. Let them know you are willing to be interviewed.

Another great option is the Free Preview Call type of event. I often use www.talkshoe.com as you can see below. This is a FREE program that allows for talking and LIVE chatting with all attendees.

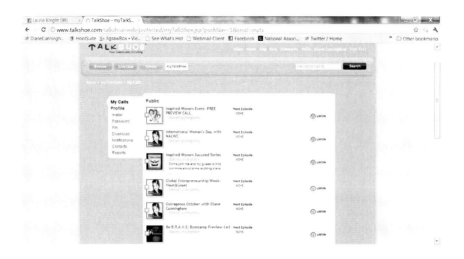

How can I use Social Media for lead generation?

Social media is the way to go now for lead generation and has become a non-negotiable.

I use my Facebook account to do the following:

- Event invitations and reminders
- Tagging people
- Notes
- Photos of products, members, or me
- Fan Pages
- Private groups
- Videos
- Links to my blog

© 2010-2013 Diane Cunningham Companies LLC

There are numerous places to engage in social media. My favorite is Facebook, but you will want to find where you fit and feel comfortable. Is that Twitter? Linked-In?

Be willing to learn a lot in this area because it is constantly changing. Just in the last week, I have used numerous new programs and gone to websites that I had no idea existed. We use Hootsuite as a big part of our social media.

What about Joint Ventures for lead generation?

A **Joint Venture** is when we team up with another person, group, or business entity for the purpose of expanding our business influence and creating a more powerful market presence.

Through the National Association of Christian Women Entrepreneurs, I create joint ventures when I invite a woman to share with the members as an expert. See below with one of our experts Julie Ziglar Norman, the daughter of Zig Ziglar, famous sales trainer and author.

Here is an example of a joint venture where I am featured with a testimonial. A **testimonial** is a statement or written affirmation in support of a particular truth, fact, or claim.

How can you help others with a testimonial? By offering a testimonial it shows your involvement with that person, company, or product and also has a link to your website.

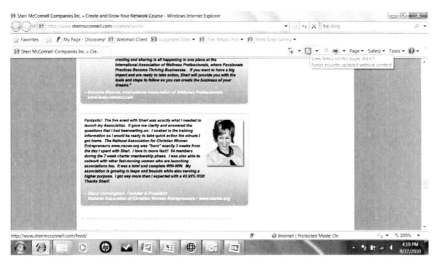

Testimonial on our NACWE home page

 © 2010-2013 Diane Cunningham Companies LLC

An example of a joint venture and a book to use for lead generation is our book Inspired Women Succeed, written by Jo Ann Fore and I. Go to www.inspiredwomensucceed.com to see.

What about Books for lead generation?

A **book** is a great form of lead generation because it gives you more credibility and allows your potential client a way to get to know you from the comfort of their own home.

Here you see a sample of my "Dear Female Entrepreneur" book that I use with clients and members and the Inspired Women Succeed book.

Go to http://nacwe.org/store to see.

This is another book that I was a part of in 2011, Smart Women Live Their WHY with Sheri McConnell. Each of these book opportunities provides a marketing tool for you. By writing your own book or being a part of another book, you set yourself up as the "go-to expert" in your field.

Go to www.smartwomenwhy.com to see!

What about Video for lead generation?

Using video is a great way to get your message out to you clients and potential clients. They can then get a "FEEL" for you and see you in action.

 © 2010-2013 Diane Cunningham Companies LLC

YouTube is a video-sharing website on which users can upload, share, and view videos.

Here is my YouTube channel under the name LifeCoachDiane, which I started in March of 2008.

Go to www.inspiredwomentv.com to see all of my videos!

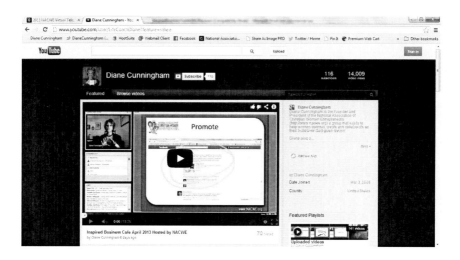

I use my Flip video camera to record most of the videos. Or I use my Iphone or Ipad. Get a system that is easy to use. You might want to incorporate both "raw" video that you do yourself and professional video. I use a combination of both.

At NACWE, I also love to use video in my email for freebies and for coaching programs.

Here is a sample of an email with a video embedded:

And we have a link to my YOUTUBE page on the NACWE site, on the right side of the page:

© 2010-2013 Diane Cunningham Companies LLC

What about Blog Talk Radio for lead generation?

BlogTalkRadio.com is a free way to produce your own online talk show. Each show is archived and can be used as a link or embedded. That means that you can post the link on your website or your facebook page for clients and customers to easily click to listen.

I now have my show branded as InspiredWomenRadio.com and have the domain name redirecting clients over to my site. I use this to interview our weekly featured members of NACWE and others.

Go to www.inspiredwomenradio.com to see!

You might also want to you use:

- Cinchcast
- Freeconferencecalling.com

What about a Blog for lead generation?

A **blog** (a blend of the term **web log**) is a type of website or part of a website. Blogs are usually maintained by an individual with regular entries of commentary, descriptions of events, or other material such as graphics or video. Entries are commonly displayed in reverse-chronological order. *Blog* can also be used as a verb, meaning *to maintain or add content to a blog.*

Most blogs are interactive, allowing visitors to leave comments and even message each other via widgets on the blogs and it is this interactivity that distinguishes them from other static websites.

Your blog is often times a place to publish your weekly articles. Articles can also be used and submitted to other online newsletter directories for publication.

Here is the blog portion of my NACWE site.
Go to www.nacwe.org/blog to SEE!

What about a newsletter or ezine for lead generation?

An ezine is a newsletter sent out periodically, monthly, weekly or daily, to subscribers who have opted to receive it. It is a very

© 2010-2013 Diane Cunningham Companies LLC

important tool for building an online business. It keeps you in contact with your potential customers, allows you to build a trusting relationship with them, gives you a chance to build your reputation and also gives you another avenue of income, via selling advertising space in your ezine.

Here is a sample of a newsletter that I sent to my entire list. You can also create sub-lists so that you can reach only certain groups such as members, or clients, or people who purchased one of your items

What about Affiliates for lead generation?

An **affiliate** (also called an Affiliate Marketer, Associate Marketer, or Publisher) is an individual that promotes a business or product on a website or through another electronic marketing medium, within the context of an Affiliate Program. Affiliates generally sign up to work with an affiliate program either directly through the program provider, or through an affiliate network that provides a variety of affiliate programs all in one place.

Affiliates are paid for their ability to send new or existing customers to others. Affiliate marketing is a common practice on the Internet, and literally tens of thousands of people make some or all of their income as affiliates.

You can see here a member of the NACWE who has just told me that she has posted her affiliate link on her website and page.

What about a Mini-Site for lead generation?

A **minisite** is a website by which companies offer information about one specific product or product group. Typically, a minisite is enhanced by various multimedia content, such as an animated, narrated introduction, and accompanied by a visual scheme which complements the product well.

Often mini-sites are in a blog format or redirected from a blog.

© 2010-2013 Diane Cunningham Companies LLC

Mini-site #1

This is my site that sells my book.

Mini-site #2

This is my site that showcases the Inspired Business Club.

The Marketing Circle

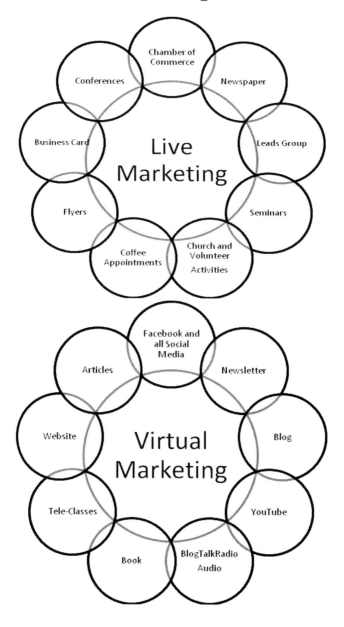

 © 2010-2013 Diane Cunningham Companies LLC

What is a marketing funnel?

A **marketing funnel** is the infrastructure or foundation of your business. It allows you to multiply your income by marketing your products and services, so you can build the business your really want and live the life you deserve. Many entrepreneurs get caught in the trap of working hours for dollars, so they only get paid when they work.   It is important to create easy ways to convert prospects into customers for life so you can create products that produce passive income.

Imagine a funnel with the wide end at the top and the narrow end at the bottom. You want to get as many people as possible into your funnel at the top and guide them through to the very bottom.

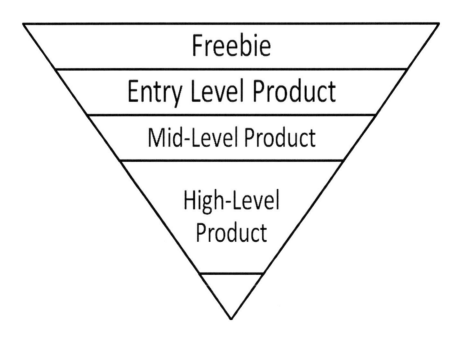

Here's how you might do this:

1. Offer a free item such as an Ebook, Report, audio class on your website, blog or landing page.
2. Once you've got their information start upselling them into low and mid-priced products or services
3. Continue to upsell customers into higher end programs or products.

The aim is to get as many prospects as possible at the top using various lead generation efforts and out of those, create loyal customers who will pay for a membership continuity program. This is what is called multiple streams of income and it is crucial to the long term success of your business.

You need multiple streams of income to thrive as a business owner. It is important for us to continue to evolve by adding new products and creating things that you can re-purpose.

As we finish up this chapter, I hope you are feeling inspired and not overwhelmed. I want to leave with you with a few more important tips. You see, we could talk about this all day, but we need to keep moving.

Tip #1: Go, Do, and Be Seen

What does it mean to "go, do, and be seen"? For me, it means being a vibrant part of my community. I love to be out and about. I love to know people and to be known. I find this to be true both where I live and also in my virtual world through my newsletter and through the amazing power of social networking. I call this networking both on the ground and in the air.

Both are crucial for us a female business owners and inspired women. If you are NOT using social media, you are missing out on an entire world of friends, colleagues, and potential business partners. Plus you might even make some sales!

 © 2010-2013 Diane Cunningham Companies LLC

Tip #2: Be your own PR agent!

We have to learn to be our own Public Relations agent. Ask if you can be on the list to be a speaker, give away a door prize, rent a booth, or be the featured member. Don't wait for someone to find you...stand up for yourself and BE LOUD!   As Christian female entrepreneurs can't be meek and mild mannered women. We need to be willing to be bold and boisterous for the sake of our cause. Be willing to talk about what you do and share your passion.

Remember Stephanie, The Trauma Queen, from module #2. She markets her business through networking events, a blog, website, and speaking engagements. www.stephanieecke.com

One of the biggest things I've learned is this... if I am to succeed, I've got to be my own PR agent. Sure, I can hire people to help me, but in the end, I'm my best PR agent. One strategy is GO, DO and BE SEEN. As a female entrepreneur, this strategy can work for me (or against me). First, I've got to go...go to networking events, speaking engagements, and workshops to enhance my skills (always making sure I have a steady supply of brochures and business cards). I've also got to DO - write articles, work on my website, create new products, and read the latest literature pertaining to my field. And last, I've got to BE SEEN. The more my name and face is in the public eye, the more well-known I will become.   Being a niche business, I depend on name recognition to get my clients.

Of course, the GO, DO and BE SEEN strategy has its downside. Like any entrepreneur, I can go too much, do too much and be seen too much. It's very important to keep balanced. It is vital for me sometimes is to Be - be quiet, be still and just Be.

Marketing Mania: Free, Cheap & Easy Ideas!

Free Products	Cheap Products & Services	Easy Ideas
Facebook.com	ConstantContact.com MailChimp.com	Create a plan
linkedin.com,	icontact.com	Use your leverage
twitter.com,	VistaPrint.com	Write an article
biznik.com,	Laminated Page	Create joint ventures
ping.fm	AudioAcrobat.com	Build relationships!
YouTube.com	Assessment Generator	
BlogTalkRadio.com Cinch-cast.com	Flip video camera	
EventBrite.com	Lulu.com	
FreeConferencePro.com	Godaddy.com	
Tungle	Aweber.com	
Blog wordpress.com	1shoppingcart.com	
Mashable.com	Vervante.com	
Talkshoe.com	Iphone	

© 2010-2013 Diane Cunningham Companies LLC

Handouts, Worksheets, and Templates

- Marketing Funnel
- My Marketing Circle-Virtual
- My Marketing Circle-Live
- One Page Marketing Plan
- 10 things I have learned about marketing
- Weekly Dreaming and Ideas
- Weekly Marketing Checklist
- Weekly Review

Marketing Checklist

Have you completed the following?

☐   Marketing Funnel

☐   My Marketing Circle-Virtual

☐   My Marketing Circle-Live

☐   One Page Marketing Plan

☐   Weekly Dreaming and Ideas

☐   Weekly Marketing Checklist

☐   Weekly Review

© 2010-2013 Diane Cunningham Companies LLC

Marketing Funnel

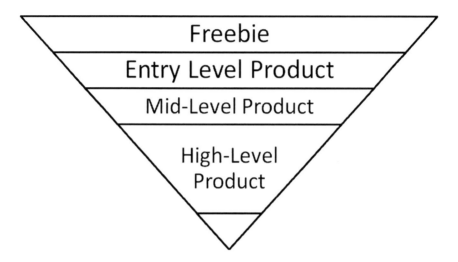

My Marketing Circle-Virtual

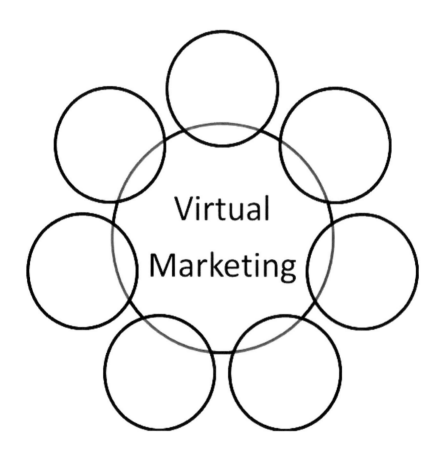

Virtual Marketing

 © 2010-2013 Diane Cunningham Companies LLC

My Marketing Circle-Live

Live

Marketing

The One Page Marketing Plan

The Strategic Plan and My Commitments

My goals for this 30 days:

Goal #1:

Goal #2:

Goal #3:

Local Marketing

□ Flyers/Postcards   □ Events   □ Seminars/Workshop

□ Newspaper (free section)   □ Bulletin boards (library, church)

□ Networking Venues   □ Other

Virtual Marketing

□ E-newsletter   □ Blog   □ Radio/BlogTalkRadio

□ Article(s)   □ Tele-Seminar or Preview call

□ Website   □ Other

My Commitment:

© 2010-2013 Diane Cunningham Companies LLC

10 Things I have learned about Marketing

#1: Marketing is FUN!

#2: Marketing is about PLANTING SEEDS!

#3: Marketing is about using your CREATIVITY!

#4: Marketing is something you do ALL THE TIME!

#5: Marketing is a LEARNED BEHAVIOR!

#6: Marketing is SIMPLE if you let it be!

#7: Marketing is about BEING YOURSELF!

#8: Marketing is about TELLING A STORY!

#9: Marketing is FICKLE, just like you!

#10: Marketing is FAST!

Get your free bonus gifts from this chapter including the One Page Marketing Plan and the Marketing Circle plus the 45 other templates just by going here now! www.nacwe.org/ToolkitResources and use the coupon code: success

Weekly Dream & Idea Space

© 2010-2013 Diane Cunningham Companies LLC

Weekly Marketing Checklist

Date	Networking Event, Article, Newsletter, etc

Weekly Review

What action(s) did I take during this week?

What were my wins or successes this week?

What were my challenges this week?

What have I learned about myself this week?

What is my focus for the upcoming week?

What progress have I made toward my goals? What has changed?

What three words would I use to describe this week?

 © 2010-2013 Diane Cunningham Companies LLC

Chapter #6
Mindset

© 2010-2013 Diane Cunningham Companies LLC

What is mindset?

Summing it all up, friends, I'd say you'll do best by filling your minds and meditating on things true, noble, reputable, authentic, compelling, gracious—the best, not the worst; the beautiful, not the ugly; things to praise, not things to curse. Put into practice what you learned from me, what you heard and saw and realized. Do that, and God, who makes everything work together, will work you into his most excellent harmonies. ~Philippians 4:8 (The Message)

Do not conform any longer to the pattern of this world, but be transformed by the renewing of your mind. Then you will be able to test and approve what God's will is -- his good, pleasing and perfect will. Romans 12:2

How do you see the world?

What is your mindset?

What mental habits are keeping you stuck or holding you back as you pursue your business?

What is a mindset?

A **mindset** is a set of assumptions, methods or notations held by one or more people or groups of people which is so established that it creates a powerful incentive within these people or groups to continue to adopt or accept prior behaviors, choices, or tools.

A mindset is often a set of beliefs or a way of thinking that determines somebody's behavior and outlook.

How does your mindset relate to being a Christian female entrepreneur?

When we begin to build a dream, to build OUR dream, it changes us. Looking at the world through the eyes of a business woman is a different view. Your mindset is made up of your world-view, your self-talk, your tapes, your culture, and more. It affects how you run your business. It is a big shift in our thinking to move from an employee mindset to that of an entrepreneur. There are so many internal levels of change that we must travel through.

For me, my mindset is a daily decision, as well as a journey. It is both. It is a choice. Many times it comes down to my self-talk.

As a believer your mindset is everything! The most important thing after accepting Christ is to renew your mind. When you take on the mind of Christ, you have a wealth of creativity. You become the paintbrush in God's hand. Each day that you face life remember you can only go as far as your mind has been renewed according to the Word of God. If you don't take time out to renew your mind everything else will ultimately fall apart. Renewing your mind prevents doubts, bitterness, depression, frustration, and anything else that can block you from walking in divine destiny from taking root in your heart. I firmly believe in servant leadership and I realize I can only be a well of life to others by first drinking from the well of Living Water.
Joslyn Johnson www.empoweringtestimony.com

Find the mindset that breaks away from the crowd and locates the shadow of His wing; there you will find rest. His gentle voice

 © 2010-2013 Diane Cunningham Companies LLC

will lead you as you set your mind on His perspective. View life as He sees it. Let His thoughts become your thoughts; after all, you have the mind of Christ.

Linda Young, Author of God Glasses, LindaYoungMinistries.com

What is self-talk?

Self-talk is "the things that an individual says to himself or herself mentally". We can have positive self-talk or negative self-talk. And the great thing is that we can begin to listen to ourselves and change our internal conversation. This is a lesson that is important for us, for our business, and for our family.

It also relates to the well known process called the self-fulfilling prophesy.

The **self-fulfilling prophecy** is defined as the positive or negative expectations about circumstances, events, or people that may affect a person's behavior toward them in a manner that he or she (unknowingly) creates situations in which those expectations are fulfilled.

When we expect to fail, we create an environment of failure. The same goes with success. If we expect to be "too busy" we begin to create a schedule that is too busy and leads to being overwhelmed.

Another part of this mindset change is the feeling of being a "fake". This is called the "**imposter syndrome**" and it happens as we begin to describe ourselves in a new way and become a new version of ourselves.

All of a sudden, you might have a website or even a store and think "What am I doing?" and secretly be saying, "I have NO idea what I am doing!"

When we become the owner, the founder, or the CEO, we have to take ownership of what that means and how it feels to describe ourselves in that way. Let me warn you, each time we move to a new level or give ourselves a new "title" this same feeling comes around again.

If you are knee-deep in the imposter syndrome, you might be saying things like this (either to yourself or out loud):

"What if they really find out that I have no idea what I am doing?"

"Am I really good enough?"

"Who really wants what I have to offer?"

"Can I really get paid for this?"

"I don't have anything to put on a website."

It is important for us to fight the "imposter syndrome" and recognize it for what it is...nothing more, nothing less. Really it is the enemy trying to keep us from moving forward. It is a distraction from all we are called to do. I would call this a DEADLY DISTRACTION.

As a Christian female entrepreneur, this will decrease the longer you are in business and the more you build up your confidence and your list of happy customers/clients. It will still arise on certain occasions but you will know how to "talk yourself off the ledge". Later in this chapter, we will discuss ways to do this.

Let's talk about some ongoing challenges that you might encounter that I love to call "mind-set mess-ups". These 8 thought patterns or beliefs, can creep up at any time and in any order. They can often arrive in a group too.

 © 2010-2013 Diane Cunningham Companies LLC

Mindset Mess-Ups

1. **EXCUSES MINDSET:** Stop making excuses for your business, your employees, your past, your office location.

2. **VICTIM MINDSET:** Don't be a victim of people who want your services but don't want to pay you, don't be a victim to that one client who takes all of your time.

3. **BAD CHOICES MINDSET:** Stop making choices that don't make sense for your business model or your current financial reality. Don't get talked into advertising that won't work for your type of business or product.

4. **BLAME MINDSET:** No more of the blame game...no more blaming the bad economy, your mother, your husband, your lack of funds, your former boss, your kids, or anyone else.

5. **DOORMAT MINDSET:** Own your own power. Stop giving away your power to whoever is in front of you. Be your own advocate.

6. **INSECURE MINDSET:** Stop putting yourself down and not giving yourself the recognition you deserve and trusting in your own strengths.

7. **OVERWHELM MINDSET:** Filling our time with appointments, projects, and tasks that do not produce revenue or increase the business. This can also include over promising with the amount of time it will take to complete a project and then getting even more overwhelmed.

8. **SELF-SABOTAGE MINDSET:** Creating a recipe for disaster and inviting failure by doing any or all of the above.

Let's look deeper into this "self-sabotage" now.

What is Self-Sabotage?

The dictionary definition of **sabotage** is "an act or process tending to hamper or hurt" or "deliberate subversion". Why on earth would we sabotage ourselves? That's a complicated answer and a simple one. We often choose to self-sabotage, as if on auto-pilot. We often want to succeed and yet know that if we do, it will change our lives. We often are so comfortable where we are, that we keep ourselves there, despite all indications that we are ready to move forward.

What is self-sabotage for you? How often are you engaging in it?

Recognizing Self-Sabotage

For me, it can be any of the following:

- Being overbooked, which leads to being overwhelmed
- Eating too much, then being distracted by the need to lose weight
- Not getting enough sleep
- Always starting new projects and then being eternally overwhelmed
- Giving away my time
- Working too hard, and not smart enough

Look at how some Christian women entrepreneurs tend to self-sabotage:

Woman #1: *Trusting someone I shouldn't trust. Failing to delegate duties for fear of betrayal.*

Woman #2: *I still struggle sometimes seeing myself as a business woman. I often have to remind myself that I am important to my company. Since I don't get up every day and go to work,*

© 2010-2013 Diane Cunningham Companies LLC

it is hard for me to see myself that way. Most of my business is done at home, on my laptop, with the kids running around.

Woman #3: *I tend to easily fall into that comparison trap of seeing what someone else is doing and then feel like I am not measuring up. I keep reminding myself that the difference between me and someone else might only be that they stepped out and I didn't. I have learned to that step and risk the failure.*

I posted this question in the private forum for members of NACWE and the following responses emerged:

What is your most common way that you self-sabotage? (being too busy, eating too much, giving away your time, not asking for help, changing directions, etc)

Rhoda Baty Not asking for help...I think it will cost me too much or they might say 'no' or I will owe them a payback...and that's the awful truth!

Connie Renee Clay Wasting time with other peoples' priorities instead of my own. Also, as a single parent, I used to put my children first. Now, God is first, I'm second, and the children are third.

Cheryl Cope Giving away my time, not having money to invest in a VA, having my boundaries violated by family members, having competing priorities....oh so many!!

Marlee D'Arco Saying "Who am I to do xyz...who do I think I am." Big ol' FAT LIE from the devil, but it's so easy to hide behind. Thankfully, I've learned to nip it in the bud.

Amanda Oney Taylor food and too much sleep

Sylvia Junt Not asking for help.

Brandi Breland-Love Not asking for help...I totally think I was placed here to help others and the hardest thing in life is for me to accept the help of others

Elizabeth DeArmond Working on other stuff, or other folks' stuff and not on MY stuff. Procrastinating and then it's too late to do it because it's irrelevant or over, giving away my time and not having boundaries.

Nicole Kirksey Perfectionism...has kept me stuck in the same place for years.

Look at these verses that address the mindset challenges and feeling like we want to give up:

Don't quit, don't give up, and don't back off...instead PRESS IN! Often when we become overwhelmed with life, with disappointments, and with our circumstances we just want to run....we want to escape...we want to give up. Instead, we need to trust God, move forward, and press into our God given purpose!

So don't throw it all away now. You were sure of yourselves then. It's still a sure thing!

But you need to stick it out, staying with God's plan so you'll be there for the promised completion.

Hebrews 10:35-36 The Message

Learning to Let Go

Let Go and Walk Away: Be willing to be done with the past and walk away. In business we have to learn the hard way sometimes and that might mean paying a price financially. Don't get stuck there. Pay your "Get Out of the Contract FEE" and move

© 2010-2013 Diane Cunningham Companies LLC

on. This is called a "sunk cost" and yes it is worth it for your peace of mind.

A sunk cost or unrecoverable cost is a cost that is not recoverable and should not influence future decisions.

Be willing to turn around, and walk away. This works for everything from a cell phone contract that is no longer working for you, or an office, or any other investment you have made that does not feel that it fits with who you are at this time. Be sure to get some outside counsel on this so that you are not acting on impulse. Then make the decision, pay the penalty and move on. Trust that this is a wise business decision.

Sometimes letting go, is not quitting. It is not failing. It can actually be the next big step in our success plan from God in learning to trust.

But we're not quitters who lose out. Oh, no! We'll stay with it and survive, trusting all the way. Hebrews 10:39 The Message

What is the Fear of Success?

When I get really honest, I know that one of my biggest fears is of SUCCESS. I talk about this often at events and a few women know exactly what I am saying and the others might not be aware of it yet. I think we as women, all come across this at different stages in our life. We might not have known what to call it, or given it a name before, but is very real. Let's see if you can relate.

To me, as a female entrepreneur, the fear of success can cause me to hold back so that I stay "in step" with my peers. It leads me to be afraid of moving ahead of what is comfortable and afraid to leave my colleagues and friends behind. I am afraid that I might have to carry the load and set the standard.

It means that I might be leading the pack and really not knowing for sure where I am going or if I will make it!

It means knowing that people might betray me, leave me, want more from me.....and that I will have to always be on my game.

It means being afraid that I am NOT WORTHY of all of that good stuff that is out there!! That I am not smart enough, thin enough, or business savvy enough to deserve it, so I might as well not even try!

How does the fear of success play out in your journey?

The solution...Mindset Miracles

So what do we do with all of this MESS? Luckily we are given some miracles from our Father who is the master at changing and improving our mindset. And by the way, God is NOT surprised at all by anything we ever think or do. Sometimes I forget that. I think I might by sneaking one by Him. Funny huh? Let's look at what I call Mindset Miracles that we can CHOOSE to engage in. Each time one of the old thoughts comes, we can recognize it and then replace it.

1. **PERMISSION. Give Yourself Permission**

   Today I give myself permission....to be strong and brave, to really show up. Today I give myself permission to be fully present. What do you need to give yourself permission to do today?

© 2010-2013 Diane Cunningham Companies LLC

2. PROCLAMATION Claim a new contract

Let us now make a proclamation. We want to create a new and improved definition of who we are and how we will show up in our business. We give ourselves what I like to call a CONTRACT, which becomes a living and breathing statement.

Some examples of this:

> "I am a successful and sought after spa owner."
>
> "I am a brave and brilliant bakery owner."
>
> "I am an innovative and in-demand photographer."
>
> "I am the CEO and President of my company."

A few years ago, I had what I call my CEO day. It was April 20th, 2010 and I was at a training event with a consultant for a program that I was ready to implement but just needed the final push to get over the hump. During the afternoon of this training, she asked us each to stand up and introduce ourselves for a 2nd time by claiming our new title as either CEO or Founder and President. What a powerful life changing moment for me!

The truth of the matter was that nothing changed that day, and everything changed that day. I woke up to my own title that I already had. I posted it on Facebook. I claimed it as my own. No one was going to give it to me. I am my own boss. I am an entrepreneur. Powerful.

What is your title? What is your contract? What will you proclaim for yourself?

3. PRACTICE Letting go of perfection

We have to allow ourselves to let go of perfection and move to a place of PRACTICE. We never arrive and the product, store, event, program will never be perfect. This is really a given for the life of an entrepreneur. We have to allow ourselves the ability to get comfortable with never being DONE. We have to trust the process and keep showing up for the practice.

In addition to these Mindset Miracles, we have 3 more P's in the process. These are crucial and non-negotiable ingredients in the Inspired Women Succeed recipe. This is a recipe that I have found works for all women.

I know that **Inspired Women Succeed** due to the following 3 ingredients:

Ingredient #1 is Passion

You are in business for yourself and I sure hope you have a passion for what you are doing. If you have lost your passion, that may be due to being overwhelmed or overworked. But I imagine you started with a HUGE passion for what you are doing.

Women entrepreneurs are a passionate group. Without passion for your business, you never would have started. Without passion, the people will perish, and so will the business. Passion is LOVE in action. Entrepreneurs take action and engage in risky behavior in order to get their message across. Being an entrepreneur is really like standing up for your cause in public and shouting to the world what you believe in.

Ingredient #2 is Persistence

Women entrepreneurs are persistent in spite of all obstacles. We keep going, taking the joys with the bumps and lumps. We show up every day for work, no matter what. We are consistent and full of faith that we will figure out the right combination of programs, products, services to create success.

 © 2010-2013 Diane Cunningham Companies LLC

We are persistent women.....never giving up! I am a marathon runner. I have finished 4 marathons (26.2 miles). I understand now that being an entrepreneur is a similar trek. We have to pace ourselves and find a rhythm. There are hills and valleys that no one but you and your inner circle will ever see. There are band aids and blisters. There are fuel stations and water stops that are crucial to your success. You might hit "the wall" and not know how you will survive. There are people ahead of you, behind you, and next to you.

Ingredient #3 is People

The 3rd ingredient is the people in your life. We need the support of key people in our life in order to succeed. Vital roles are played by the family of an entrepreneur. To have the support of your spouse and/or immediate family is critical. Key friends are crucial for ongoing support and encouragement. The right mix of coaches, mentors, and visionary consultants can make or break you. We will cover more on this subject in the Mentor chapter.

So now, how do I go forward? What do you need to know? This is what I call my Be BRAVE system.

How to Be BRAVE!

Each day we have an opportunity to be brave.   In 2010, I chose the theme for my year as "Be BRAVE". I made intentional choices to take on things that scared me and I might have shied away from before. Being brave is about business and about life. It is about conversations and clarity. It is about shining my light for all to see. It is a **mindset shift** that affects all of us.

Let me give you a few examples from my year of BRAVE:

- I went flying with in a small private plane
- In May 2010, I launched the association www.nacwe.org and promoted myself to CEO.
- I sang a Shania Twain song in front of 50 people at a karaoke party

So as I have been doing this myself, and with a few girlfriends, I began to mention this to my clients and colleagues. Then I thought....how can I make this a **movement** that more people can join? How can we all BE BRAVE together?

I then created the 30 day free series of emails. Go to www.be-bravetoday.com to get registered and start your 30 day journey.

I don't know about you but I am done waiting around. I am done sitting on the sidelines watching my life go by. I am stepping out in new directions and with bold abandon.

Whatever you are dealing with.....you need courage. You need to BE BRAVE!

B.R.A.V.E. is about being the **Bold Risky Adventurous Visionary Entrepreneur** that you are! It is a mindset shift and attitude change. It is a mantra. This year, each time I feel that old familiar feeling of fear, and have a thought of NOT moving forward, I call up my Be BRAVE attitude and say YES!

Tricks that I use to help me Be B.R.A.V.E.:

Music: Listen to music in the car or the office, that inspires me

Friends: Call a friend who knows me and gives me courage.

 © 2010-2013 Diane Cunningham Companies LLC

Exercise: When I need to get my mind back in the right place, it is often due to my need to get my body moving

Quotes: The perfect quote can help me to see beyond the moment and keep moving forward

Let's hear from Sandy Myers, who attended my Be Brave Bootcamp earlier this year:

Being BRAVE changes things. Going from an employee to an entrepreneur was an unexpected dream come true for me. The company I worked for went through a massive lay off, and my position was eliminated 3 weeks after my husband I moved into our first home. We were scared but we made it through the first four months of the year successfully. I began to do some freelance work at home, and I was able to use my available time to finish my certification in Life Coaching. I began a coaching business in faith. God blessed my efforts, and I was given opportunities to speak, and I met some wonderful people during the summer. Diane was one of my divine connections. I took her Be BRAVE Business Bootcamp course and I learned how to take action in my business. I was not ready for that the challenge that came with changing my mindset. I did not want an expensive hobby coaching people for free. I wanted to be an entrepreneur and build a successful business. I felt like I was wearing high heels for the first time. You know… that awkward yet proud feeling you have of dressing up and walking taller. The only thing was there is a learning curve with heels. In the beginning you are prone to twisting your foot and falling, getting used to the new height and walking gracefully at the same time. You just keep moving forward, risking looking foolish sometimes.

Here is an excerpt of an email I sent Diane towards the end of the course:

"God really has blessed my efforts the past 6 weeks, but I feel that I am hitting a new hurdle, that is different than what I have faced in the past. Who can I share with about what I am feeling? I feel alone. I feel that God is taking me through a transformation process into something unfamiliar. Having an entrepreneur mindset is very different for me, but I welcome the challenge. I did not expect all these changes to bring such confusing emotions. I am making changes in myself, and taking action towards a dream and it feels new. I should be excited right? It is a new normal, and I feel like I am doing something different, almost wrong...but I know this not a correct way of thinking. I have always ministered to people, and I love to teach in a church setting. The journaling assignment you gave us for class has really affected my mind. I need clients. I need to value my time and think like a CEO. I want to get paid, and I am so used to using my gifting for free through church. You know, although I feel these new emotions, I have HOPE in my heart that all these changes are for my good."

Sandy Myers www.sandymyers.com

How will you choose to be brave? What will you do differently?

"Everything is possible for him who believes." Mark 9:23

"Not everything that is faced can be changed, but nothing can be changed until it is faced." James Baldwin

© 2010-2013 Diane Cunningham Companies LLC

Handouts, Worksheets, and Templates

- Imposter Syndrome Survey

- Self-Sabotage quiz

- Doubt Awareness

- Comfort Zone Check In

- I give myself permission

- My proclamation

- My Be BRAVE plan

- Weekly Dreaming and Ideas

- Weekly Marketing Checklist

- Weekly Review

Mindset Checklist

Have you completed the following?

- ☐ Imposter Syndrome Survey
- ☐ Self-Sabotage Quiz
- ☐ Doubt Awareness
- ☐ Comfort Zone Check-In
- ☐ I give myself permission to
- ☐ My proclamation
- ☐ My Be BRAVE Plan
- ☐ Weekly Dreaming and Ideas
- ☐ Weekly Marketing Checklist
- ☐ Weekly Review

© 2010-2013 Diane Cunningham Companies LLC

Imposter Syndrome Survey

When I am feeling like a FAKE, I hear myself saying:

Self-Sabotage Quiz

I self-sabotage my business and my life by doing these things:

Self-Sabotage Thought/Behavior	How this keeps me stuck:

© 2010-2013 Diane Cunningham Companies LLC

Doubt Awareness

My biggest areas of doubt in my business/company are:

Comfort Zone Check-In

This tool is to help you see where you are stuck and how you might be able to move from this place. We love our routines, even if they are not "bearing fruit". Change is so challenging that we readily move back to our "comfy chair" and stay put. My hope for you is that you will see what is "blocking" you and make a choice.

What has fear stolen from me?

How do I stop the fears?

How do I prepare for obstacles?

How do I intentionally get out of my "comfort zone"?

Who, What, Where is my "comfort zone"?

© 2010-2013 Diane Cunningham Companies LLC

I give myself permission to

My Proclamation!

I am a....

© 2010-2013 Diane Cunningham Companies LLC

Weekly Dream & Idea Space

Weekly Marketing Checklist

Date	Networking Event, Article, Newsletter, etc

© 2010-2013 Diane Cunningham Companies LLC

Weekly Review

What action(s) did I take during this week?

What were my wins or successes this week?

What were my challenges this week?

What have I learned about myself this week?

What is my focus for the upcoming week?

What progress have I made toward my goals? What has changed?

What three words would I use to describe this week?

© 2010-2013 Diane Cunningham Companies LLC

Chapter #7
Mentors

© 2010-2013 Diane Cunningham Companies LLC

What is mentoring?

As iron sharpens iron, so one man sharpens another. Proverbs 27:17

Who is your mentor?

What do you want to learn during this phase of your business growth?

Are you in a mastermind group?

I have learned so much about what it means to run a business and succeed as a female entrepreneur through these valuable relationships with other women and men. Since the start of my career, I have sought out the wisdom of others as often as possible through events, websites, seminars, and one-on-one experiences. This learning and growing has saved me thousands of dollars on unneeded products and services. I believe in the ancient wisdom that when the pupil is ready the teacher will appear. I love to learn and gather the wisdom shared by others.

What is a mentor?

A **mentor** is a trusted friend, counselor or teacher, usually a more experienced person. Some professions have "mentoring programs" in which newcomers are paired with more experienced people, who advise them and serve as examples as they advance. Schools sometimes offer mentoring programs to new students, or students having difficulties.

Today mentors provide expertise to less experienced individuals to help them advance their careers, enhance their education, and build their networks. In many different arenas people have benefited from being part of a mentoring relationship.

Mentoring can be an employee training system under which a senior or more experienced individual (the mentor) is assigned to act as an advisor, counselor, or guide to a trainee. The mentor is responsible for providing support to, and feedback on, the individual in his or her charge.

I love mentoring and I have had the great honor to be able to mentor many in my life path. This is because of the life-long mentors that God has given me as examples. I think of my mentor Janelle Thayer in college and my mentor Lynn Camp at my first job. I think of when I was the Mentor Coordinator for the Christian Women's Job Corps in 2009 and when I mentored others who wanted to run their first marathon and raise money for the Leukemia & Lymphoma Society. I think of one of my current mentors, L.O. Nelson, at the Small Business Development Center in Wichita Falls, Texas.

There are many types of mentoring relationships. We need to be on both sides as mentor and mentee. I believe whole heartedly that we need both. I have had mentors for years that have expanded my realm of understanding and helped me to SEE myself bigger and move to the next level of my journey in awareness.

I love my coaches, my mentors, and my colleagues and I love to engage with each of them to learn the next piece of my puzzle.

Mentors can also be someone that you take a class with or work with at a seminar. It could even be someone you have never met in person but you learn from their materials (books, newsletters, CD's, and other information products). A few years ago, I had the privilege of attending a conference where Zig Ziglar was one

© 2010-2013 Diane Cunningham Companies LLC

of our speakers. Zig Ziglar has been a mentor and inspiration for thousands and thousands of people. It was an honor to see him and hear him share with our group. He has now passed away but I was blessed to also meet his daughter and know her as a colleague, friend, and a member of NACWE. His words of wisdom have left a legacy.

Another mentor that I recently had the honor of meeting was John C. Maxwell. I took the chance to get my photo taken and also gave him a copy of my book.

Look at what these women shared about mentoring relationships:

Few investments pay dividends like that of being a mentor. Be intentional about giving of your experiences, your knowledge, your discernment and your time to someone coming along a path you have already traveled is an act of service I find to be unmatched. When trust is established and hope is instilled, the relationship can go far beyond that of just two people talking. Today, many of us are benefactors of mentors along the way and as Christians, none is more meaningful to me than Paul who mentored many who have paved the way for the church today.

Cathy Alford from www.LifeWorksResourceGroup.com

I have come to learn that mentoring is a vital key to success and progress in all areas of my life, whether it is as a mom, a friend, a business woman, and a wife. Learning from others who have already walked some of the paths I am on is such an encouragement. One...to know and understand that I'm not alone or the "only" one needing help and advice and Two: to gain wisdom, insight, and ideas that I might not have otherwise known.

Submitted by Kelly Kinch with SendOutCards.com/kkinch

A great book on mentoring is <u>Connecting: The Mentoring Relationships You Need to Succeed in Life</u>, written by Dr. Bobby Clinton.

Here is how he describes mentoring with 4 unique mentoring options:

Intensive Mentoring - This is a proactive method where there is a discipler, Spiritual director or a coach to help move a person from one place to another regarding something very important in their life. He says that this form of mentoring takes a time commitment. This is a more formalized type of mentoring and people who have this type of mentoring in their life are most fortunate.

Occasional Mentoring - I would call this kind of mentoring a counselor, teacher, or even a sponsor. Basically, this is a person who comes in to your life for a season (or even seasonal) to help you through something you are working on or learning. It may not be as formal as intensive mentoring. It could be a class,

 © 2010-2013 Diane Cunningham Companies LLC

counseling appointment or a short term commitment to work through an issue.

Passive Mentoring - We all have these types of mentors. They are found in historical or contemporary teaching and books. Some of my mentors in this area are Max Lucado, Laurie Beth Jones, and Tommy Newberry. You might think of Joyce Meyers or Paula White.

Peer Modeling and Mentoring - We can never underestimate the power of peer mentors. I am in numerous peer mentoring relationships that I love. I am always amazed how much mentoring takes place in those groups. When the scripture says, "iron sharpens iron," we can understand how important these kinds of relationships are for our life.

As I write about mentoring, I see the faces and recall our telephone conversations, from the beginning of our journey together until now. What an honor and blessing to be able to bring HIS message of love and encouragement to these precious, chosen women; to be a part of their destiny.

Jeanna Scott, RN and Life Coach www.jeannascott.com

Isaiah 60:1 says it so well: "Arise and shine, for your light has come, and the glory of the LORD has risen upon you……."

What if mentoring goes BAD?

On the flip side, many women have been hurt deeply by a negative experience with another female mentor. This creates a deep sense of sadness in me. Of all things, we should be here for one another to build a bridge across.

We need to be careful in our mentoring relationships to follow these basic guidelines:

- Clearly define the roles, expectations and boundaries
- Decide on level of commitment
- Remain flexible
- Learn from what works
- Be on guard against competitive thoughts
- Not expect one person to hold all of your answers

What does it mean to "bless and release?"

Let me offer a real story from my journey. In 2009, my business was not moving as fast as I wanted it to. The economy was changing. I had become more "wishy-washy" with my brand and really had no defined niche market. Also during this time, I felt like I needed to gain more training and thus opted to change directions and go under another programs business umbrella. It was during this year, that I also experienced a change in relationship with a mentor. I spent hours thinking about each of these situations and decisions and how they would affect me both emotionally and business-wise.

I spent a few days shedding tears in my office as I made very tough decisions to leave some organizations and to join others. I took a stand and I spoke the truth. What a relief!

This process changes my view of mentoring. It gave me a glimpse into what I call "bless and release". It is critical that we not force our views on others that we are mentoring. Or create a sense of need or dependence. This was a defining moment for me to listen to God, trust my gut, seek wise counsel, and then surrender. I did not give up my truth. I agreed to disagree and I honored what I felt to be true. We want to be wise women who are leading others. We do not want to hold someone back from where they need to go. As mentors, our job is to share our knowledge and

 © 2010-2013 Diane Cunningham Companies LLC

experience, not create a clone. And a mentoring relationship is often not an employee/employer relationship. We have to be mindful of that also.

The most important lesson I learned from this is that one mentor cannot and should not, give us all that we need. There is a time and a season. We have so much to learn from so many mentors over the course of our lives. This was a great lesson in leadership for me, and how I want to show up in my mentoring relationships

What about leadership?

All of this relates to leadership. I see women avoiding leadership and not understanding it. The truth is we are all leaders. You might be leading your team, a company, or your children. But have no doubt, people are watching you and following you. Be aware of your influence and your presence. Who is leading you? Who is following you?

What is a leader?

A **leader** is a person who guides others toward a common goal, showing the way by example, and creating an environment in which other team members feel actively involved in the entire process. A leader is not the boss of the team but, instead, the person that is committed to carrying out the mission of the venture.

Who are some of leaders that have influenced you?

What type of leader are you?

Do you see yourself as a leader or a follower? Why?

In its essence, leadership in an organizational role involves (1) establishing a clear vision, (2) sharing (communicating) that vision with others so that they will follow willingly, (3) providing the information, knowledge, and methods to realize that vision, and (4) coordinating and balancing the conflicting interests of all members or stakeholders. A leader comes to the forefront in case of crisis, and is able to think and act in creative ways in difficult situations. Unlike management, leadership flows from the core of a personality and cannot be taught.

We often say that leadership is "caught not taught" and this is often done through training and may be enhanced through coaching or mentoring.

Let's look now at some ways to improve our mentoring and leadership for ourselves and for those we mentor.

The 3 A's: Awareness, Accountability, and Action

I believe that the non-negotiable ingredients are awareness, accountability, and action. Let's take a look at each one.

What is awareness?

Awareness is the state or ability to perceive, to feel, or to be conscious of events, objects or sensory patterns. In this level of consciousness, sense data can be confirmed by an observer without necessarily implying understanding. More broadly, it is the state or quality of being aware of something.

© 2010-2013 Diane Cunningham Companies LLC

What is your level of awareness?

How will you improve your understanding of yourself?

How can awareness help your mentoring relationships?

What is accountability?

Accountability is the obligation of an individual, firm, or institution to account for its activities, accept responsibility for them, and to disclose the results in a transparent manner. It also includes the responsibility for money or other entrusted property.

How and to whom are you accountable?

What is your level of commitment?

How can accountability improve your mentoring?

What is action?

Action is the state or process of acting or doing. It can also be organized activity to accomplish an objective.

What is your level of activity?

What ways can you help your mentee's take action?

How can you take action to set the example?

We need awareness, accountability and action to improve our mentoring and to help us be better mentors. Let's dive deeper into each of these areas to see how you can use them for your business both now and in the years to come.

"Whatever course you decide upon, there is always someone to tell you that you are wrong. There are always difficulties arising which tempt you to believe that your critics are right. To map out a course of action and follow it to an end requires courage."

-Ralph Waldo Emerson

Types of Accountability

© 2010-2013 Diane Cunningham Companies LLC

What is coaching?

Coaching refers to the activity of a coach in developing the abilities of coachees or clients. Coaching tends to focus on the achievement by coachees of a goal or specific skill. Methodologies for coaching are positioned away from the directive or the facilitative, and rest on accompanying clients within a dialogue that will allow emerging patterns and solutions to surface. Coaching lies out of the scale between mentoring and training on one end, and psychotherapy and counseling at the other.

My first business coach was Jackie Nagel, from Synnovatia. She was and continues to be one of my biggest cheerleaders. I found her as a result of a referral from a friend who had also done coaching with her. I knew that I could not afford her, but that I could NOT keep going without her. I made the investment and commitment. It was a very wise choice.

At the insistence of a dear friend, after listening to me struggle with time management, staffing issues and, of course, the reduction in income that was being felt due to leaving a very secure salaried position to produce on a commission only basis, I decided to humble her and meet with a coach. Although I was very skeptical in the beginning, the ability to have a listening ear, an encouraging word and strategic criticisms all wrapped up in one...WOW! Marguerite Love, Farmers Insurance

I love coaching: being coached and coaching women and leaders in ministry! Growth is all about change, and change is hard! It involves pain--letting go of the old to make room for the new! Coaching gives you the courage, the tools, the heart and the plan to change--in spite of fear and pain, because it gives you someone to walk that journey of change with you!

Karen Sinn www.lookingupministries.com

What is an Advisory Council?

According to Entrepreneur.com an **Advisory Board or Advisory Council** is a group of individuals who've been selected to help advise a business owner regarding any number of business issues, including marketing, sales, financing, expansion and so on; a body that advises the board of directors and management of a corporation but does not have authority to vote on corporate matters.

What a wise addition for all of us female entrepreneurs to add a team of advisors. This could be either locally or virtually with phone calls and meetings. As I think about this, my advisory team currently consists of my website designer, a virtual assistant, my weekly mastermind group, my financial advisor, the Small Business Development Center, and my husband.

In addition to my mastermind group, I have an advisory board filled with people I trust who I know won't always agree with me. I know that this is a good thing because I knew they would challenge me. I have a variety of people that might challenge me a little bit so they could speak truth into me and not be afraid to hurt my feelings. Kristi Olson www.purposereleased.com

What is a Mastermind Group?

The MasterMind concept was introduced by Napoleon Hill almost 100 years ago in his best-selling book Think and Grow Rich. He wrote, "No two minds ever come together without thereby creating a third, invisible intangible force, which may be likened to a third mind." And doesn't this fit right in with a familiar verse that says "For wherever two or more are gathered together in My name, I am there in the midst of them." Matthew 18:20

© 2010-2013 Diane Cunningham Companies LLC

Mastermind groups offer a combination of masterminding, peer brainstorming, education, accountability and support in a group setting to sharpen your business and personal skills. A mastermind group helps you and your mastermind group members achieve success. There is synergy of energy, commitment and excitement that participants bring to a mastermind group.

A **mastermind** is a group of likeminded individuals that are working towards success together and willing to invest in each other.

I have been a part of groups that meet in person and groups that meet by phone. Some groups have met weekly and others have met yearly for a powerful weekend experience. I am in one group that has been meeting for one year by phone. We take turns "hosting" the call and taking the lead. We benefit from the wisdom and experience of all of us combined! I have found it to be a huge blessing in my life.

In a mastermind group, you learn to speak the truth because there is no place to hide. You feel safe as you hear other members speaking the truth too. You build relationships that last years, long after the group has ended.

Speak the Truth

What does it mean to for you to **speak the truth**?

The phrase "speak the truth" comes from a well known bible verse that says speak the truth in love. "But speaking the truth in love..." ~Ephesians 4:15   There is a huge difference in the way people speak the truth. As women we often learn early in our lives to stay quiet or not say what we really think or feel. This takes a lot of "un-doing" to help us learn to be willing to start talking and to begin to stand up tall and ask for what we need.

As women business owners, we have to get really good at speaking the truth. This could be by asking for the sale, confronting a team issue with your staff, or casting a vision to investors.

I have experienced this **SPEAK THE TRUTH** principle many times over my years as an entrepreneur both on the giving side and the receiving side. The truth really will set you free and yet our tendency is to run from it.

We, as female entrepreneurs, have truth to understand each day. What truth do you bring to your clients, customers, members, or affiliates?

Speaking the truth is a powerful way of claiming who you are as a female entrepreneur. When we speak the truth, we empower others to do the same. We share information, support, laughter, and even tears. I find immense value in this process and thus created mastermind coaching groups for my own clients.

What is a Peer Mentor?

A peer mentor is someone that you might consider a colleague or maybe even a competitor, but they are crucial in your success. My long time peer mentor is Kelly Thorne Gore, the founder of iBloom. We met over 5 years ago when were both attending the same coach training program. We became fast friends and have been crucial to each other's growth and success. We set up official appointments monthly and for many years spoke daily by phone as we were trouble shooting issues or questions. We used each other as another pair or eyes and ears. I love Kelly and feel honored to call her my friend and a peer mentor. An important side note here is that Kelly is 10 years younger than I am. Age has nothing to do with who the right mentor is for you.

© 2010-2013 Diane Cunningham Companies LLC

What about Training?

Ongoing training is crucial for our success. Over the last 5 years I have intentionally invested in a wide variety of training opportunities and conferences with people who are all over the map.

I love the conference atmosphere and the connections that are made in the room. Over the last year I have learned from Milana Leshinski, Sheri McConnell, and Carrie Wilkerson. What a blessing to invest in this life changing time! I encourage you to set aside a portion of your budget each year for your ongoing training. This is another area that I believe is non-negotiable. If we are not getting the relevant information for our field, we will be left behind compared to our competition.

What is an Action Plan?

An **action plan** is steps that must be taken, or activities that must be performed for a strategy to succeed.

An action plan has three major elements

1. Specific tasks: what will be done and by whom.
2. Time horizon: when will it be done.
3. Resource allocation: what specific funds are available for specific activities.

What is your action plan?

What is your Action Plan and how will you implement it?

Do you have your goals written down?

What is your monthly goal?

Support System

A **support system** system is a network of supporters. This is a group of family, friends, colleagues, or professionals available to help a person or organization when required.

Who is in your support system? Do you feel supported? Do you have wise counsel? We have to be very aware of the choices we have to "invest" in ourselves. We need to be intentional about that investment with books, classes, education, people, and life choices. We also have to look at how we can maintain change.

As a coach, my goal is to help my clients to speak the truth about where they are in their business and in their life.

As a consultant, I look for areas of improvement in marketing or product development and offer insight from my vantage point.

As a mentor, I want to share my heart-felt wisdom and life experiences from the journey with no strings attached.

I often joke that being an entrepreneur is "not for the faint of heart" because it causes you to confront the things that others do not have to look at. There is no place to hide and no one to blame.

As a female entrepreneur, we have the amazing gift of owning our own small piece of the world, of building our dream, of launching our vision....that is truth in action.

We are brave women, who are leaders. We have so much wisdom to share from all that we have learned in our past. And each day holds another "tote bag" full of learning opportunities.

 © 2010-2013 Diane Cunningham Companies LLC

Handouts, Worksheets, and Templates

- 10 Ways to be a great mentor!
- Mentoring Quiz
- Leadership Assessment
- Support Systems and Maintaining Change

10 Ways to be a Great Mentor!

Be Honest: Share what you have learned, both good and bad. Your honesty is what they are seeking.

Be Genuine: Your mentee wants to see the authentic you, not a fake. Don't feel like you have to know all of the answers.

Be a Resource: Guide your mentee to information (classes, websites, books, and people) that could be of great value. Don't assume they know....ask and then connect the dots.

Be Timely: Be a great example of time management. Be on time to your appointments. Do what you say you will do. Set the pace.

Be a Life-Long Learner: Keep current on your field and others. Be on the lookout for your next opportunity to learn. Take a new class!

Be Inspiring: Help your mentee become a better person. Focus on the strengths you see in them. Encourage and motivate them with your words.

Be willing: Be willing to go the extra mile, to ask the hard questions, to give the feedback, to make the phone call. Be willing.

Be a Role Model: Understand that your mentee will become more and more like you...are you setting the example?

Be Consistent: Show them how to be consistent and stay focused for the long haul. Life is a marathon, not a sprint. Help them to see it in action.

Be Yourself: Allow your mentee to really see you...the true you! Most great lessons in life are caught, not taught. Be you, and keep becoming a better you.

© 2010-2013 Diane Cunningham Companies LLC

Mentors Checklist

Have you completed the following?

- ☐ Mentoring Quiz
- ☐ Leadership Assessment
- ☐ Support System and Maintaining Change
- ☐ Weekly Dreaming and Ideas
- ☐ Weekly Marketing Checklist
- ☐ Weekly Review

Get your mentoring quiz and leadership assessment as our FREE gift today. Go to www.nacwe.org/ToolkitResources to get all of the 47 templates by using the coupon code: success

Mentoring Quiz

This tool is to help you as you consider the mentoring relationships you have had in your life, and how you can mentor others.

Who are the mentors I have had during my life?

- Growing up years?
- High School years?
- College years?
- Working years?
- Family years?
- Others

What lessons have I learned from each mentor?

Who have I mentored during my life? Formally or informally?

What lessons have I learned from being a mentor?

What is the hardest part of being a mentor?

© 2010-2013 Diane Cunningham Companies LLC

Leadership Assessment

This tool is to help you consider your leadership abilities and how you can build on them. My hope is that you will be able to increase your influence and improve your skills so that you make a bigger impact. You are a leader, no matter if you describe yourself as a leader or not. People are watching you and following you. What are you teaching?

Who are the leaders that I admire? (Past or Present, Living or Dead)

What type of leadership opportunities have I had in the past?

What type of leadership activities am I involved in currently?

What qualities do I want to improve in myself as a leader?

What areas do I find challenging as a leader?

Support System and Maintaining Change

People I trust who support me:

Specific ways I am willing to invest in myself:

- Now....

- In the future:...

Obstacles I will eliminate and/or manage:

How I will feel a year from now when I reach one of my goals/dreams?

What keeps me from maintaining change in my life?

 © 2010-2013 Diane Cunningham Companies LLC

Weekly Dream & Idea Space

Weekly Marketing Checklist

Date	Networking Event, Article, Newsletter, etc

© 2010-2013 Diane Cunningham Companies LLC

Weekly Review

What action(s) did I take during this week?

What were my wins or successes this week?

What were my challenges this week?

What have I learned about myself this week?

What is my focus for the upcoming week?

What progress have I made toward my goals? What has changed?

What three words would I use to describe this week?

© 2010-2013 Diane Cunningham Companies LLC

Chapter #8

Connections

© 2010-2013 Diane Cunningham Companies LLC

What are your Connections?

Two are better than one, because they have a good reward for their toil. For if they fall, one will lift up his fellow. But woe to him who is alone when he falls and has not another to lift him up! Again, if two lie together, they keep warm, but how can one keep warm alone? And though a man might prevail against one who is alone, two will withstand him—a threefold cord is not quickly broken. Ecclesiastes 4:9-12

How are you connecting?

What opportunities are right in front of you?

Who will be a vital part of your team?

We have talked about mentors and we have talked about creating a support system. We know that there is a power in connecting. We are not meant to live in a vacuum or try to do all of this by ourselves.

What does it mean for you to connect?

My heart is all about connections. I love to make connections with people, I love to connect people to each other, and I love to connect people to a resource that might solve their challenge.

What is a connection?

A **connection** is the linking of people or things together. It can be the joining of people, things, or events.

It is how God wired us, to want to be with others in relationships, marriages, and families. For me, a connection is more than just being in the vicinity of others. It comes down to being close on a heart to heart level. It means talking about important things and sharing life together.

What about Community?

A **community** is a group of people who live in the same area or the area in which they live. It can also be a group of people with a common background or with shared interests within society.

Where is your community?

Where is your community? What tribe do you belong to?

I created the National Association of Christian Women Entrepreneurs so that we could have a tribe and find each other. What a wild ride that has been! There is power and leverage in the connection and/or association. There is a power in the WE-ness of a group. I am not alone and it gives me strength.

I find myself being more and more protective of the association and the members. It feels like I am protecting my family, which makes perfect sense when you think of a tribe. We talked about tribes in chapter #2 when we looked at your people and your niche. Now let's take a look at the definition of an association.

© 2010-2013 Diane Cunningham Companies LLC

What is an association?

The BusinessDictionary.com says that an **association** is the gathering of people for a common cause or purpose and/or the relationship between two data items where one is dependent on, or causes, the other.

According to Wikipedia, a **voluntary association** or **union** is a group of individuals who enter into an agreement as volunteers to form a body (or organization) to accomplish a purpose.

A **professional association** (also called a **professional body**, **professional organization**, or **professional society**) is usually a non-profit organization seeking to further a particular profession, the interests of individuals engaged in that profession, and the public interest.

The roles of these professional associations have been variously defined: "A group of people in a learned occupation who are entrusted with maintaining control or oversight of the legitimate practice of the occupation;"also a body acting "to safeguard the public interest;" organizations which "represent the interest of the professional practitioners," and so "act to maintain their own privileged and powerful position as a controlling body."

There is unique power in an association model and it is the reason that the National Association of Christian Women Entrepreneurs has been so successful. (Find out more and come join us at www.nacwe.org)

Are you ready to join our association and be surrounded by women who have the same values and beliefs as you do while building your business? Go here now and get connected....we can't wait to meet you! Join our sisterhood here: nacwe.org/nacwe-membership/

What does it mean to collaborate?

Collaboration is a recursive process where two or more people or organizations work together in an intersection of common goals — for example, an intellectual endeavor that is creative in nature—by sharing knowledge, learning and building consensus. Most collaboration requires leadership, although the form of leadership can be social within a decentralized and egalitarian group. In particular, teams that work collaboratively can obtain greater resources, recognition and reward when facing competition for finite resources. Collaboration is also present in opposing goals exhibiting the notion of adversarial collaboration, though this is not a common case for using the word.

Some of the best ways to collaborate are through joint ventures, partnerships, outsourcing, teams, and affiliates.

What is a joint venture?

A **joint venture** is a business enterprise jointly undertaken by two or more companies, who share the initial investment, risks, and profits.

I have done many joint ventures over the years, long before I even understood what the phrase meant. Kelly Thorne Gore, from iBloom.us and I have offered training together for years. We have co-taught groups and lead retreats. Another joint venture that I didn't understand fully at the time was when I partnered with a local spa owner Dawn Thompson to train her staff and offer ongoing coaching.

No person is an island. When we work together we can get even more accomplished.   People say too many cooks in the kitchen

© 2010-2013 Diane Cunningham Companies LLC

spoils the soup, but I just say, too many cooks in the kitchen, with no direction... spoils the soup....there is a difference. Let's collaborate! Dr. Debra Brooks www.drbrooksspeaks.com

I would never be where I am if it were not for those who have partnered with me through the years. Not only do they help me to establish credibility and trust, but they also help me to continue to work hard to birth those projects that just might collect dust without their encouragement. Nothing is like having a friend alongside of us cheering us all along the way!

Cindy Rushton www.cindyrushton.com

What is outsourcing?

Outsourcing is contracting, sub-contracting, or 'externalizing' non-core activities to free up cash, personnel, time, and facilities for activities where the firm holds competitive advantage. Firms having strengths in other areas may contract-out data processing, legal, manufacturing, marketing, payroll accounting, or other aspects of their businesses to concentrate on what they do best and thus reduce average unit cost. Outsourcing is often an integral part of downsizing or reengineering.

Let me give you an example of outsourcing from my business.

I have my virtual assistant Kathy in Florida who helps me with my newsletter, blogging, mini-sites, reports, and many other things by way of email.

I have my wordpress blog web designer Sam Baja who takes care of the National Association of Christian Women Entrepreneurs website and updates.

I have my social media manager Alison in Kentucky who helps me behind the scenes to get my message across.

I believe in order to get the most work completed, and the best work done, as business owners it is worth investing in a team of people that can share their skills and expertise to get the job done. Let others share their brilliance with you and watch as you all shine together.

Alyssa Avant, http://CreativeVAPartner.com

Building your Team

What is a team? How might you build your team?

A **team** is a group of people with a full set of complementary skills required to complete a task, job, or project. Team members operate with a high degree of interdependence, share authority and responsibility for self-management, are accountable for the collective performance, and work toward a common goal and shared rewards. A team becomes more than just a collection of people when a strong sense of mutual commitment creates synergy, thus generating performance greater than the sum of the performance of its individual members.

What is a virtual team?

A **virtual team** — also known as a **geographically dispersed team** (GDT) —is a group of individuals who work across time, space, and organizational boundaries with links strengthened by webs of communication technology.

Members of virtual teams communicate electronically, so they may never meet face to face. Virtual teams are made possible by

© 2010-2013 Diane Cunningham Companies LLC

the amazing tools we have at our finger tips through social media and various web tools.

This process has actually created a new field and new jobs. There in now what is called an Online Business Manager, and certification programs to become an Online Business Manager.

What Is An Online Business Manager?

According to Brenda M. Violette, who owns VBS Online Business Management, the official definition of an Online Business Manager (OBM) is a virtually based support professional who manages online based businesses, including the day-to-day management of projects, operations, management of team members, metrics management, and development of multiple streams of income. Her tagline is "managing your business so that you can focus on what you do best!"

I have been slowly adding to my virtual team for NACWE. We have a PR Director, a Membership Coordinator, a Spiritual Director, a Forum Coordinator, and a Comprehensive Assistant.

Each of these women are gifted and being used to help expand our reach. A virtual team can connect through email, phone calls, social media, forums, webinars, and much more. The power of technology is amazing in how you can create an opportunity for growth and learning.

I love how the internet has evolved. For many years, I was sooo isolated in business. I had to do E-V-E-R-Y-T-H-I-N-G!! Now, I not only get to do what I do best, but I can work with a team where everyone brings their best to the table. It is so much easier to reach for the call as we use our gifts and talents together! Cindy Rushton from www.cindyrushton.com

What is an affiliate?

Affiliate marketing is a marketing practice in which a business rewards one or more affiliates for each visitor or customer brought about by the affiliate's marketing efforts. Examples include rewards sites, where users are rewarded with cash or gifts, for the completion of an offer, and the referral of others to the site. The industry has four core players: the merchant (also known as 'retailer' or 'brand'), the network, the publisher (also known as 'the affiliate'), and the customer. The market has grown in complexity to warrant a secondary tier of players, including affiliate management agencies, super-affiliates and specialized third parties vendors.

There is amazing benefit to offering an affiliate program. It creates a built in referral process and a way to offer a gift of compensation to your referral partner. It is a win-win. I tell my clients about programs, books, other coaches, trainings, events, etc all the time. This is a way to get paid for what you would be doing anyway.

How can you use the affiliate concept in your business?

What can we do to intentionally cultivate our relationships and build our connectivity quotient?

To learn more about NACWE's affiliate program,
go to nacwe.org/affiliate-info/

What does it mean to cultivate?

To **cultivate** means to grow or tend a plant or crop, to promote the growth of, to nurture, to foster, and to seek the acquaintance of or make friends with.

© 2010-2013 Diane Cunningham Companies LLC

7 Key ingredients for building your connections

I have found that there are 7 key ingredients to improve, build, and multiply my connections. Here there are:

Ingredient #1 is Awareness

It is important to be aware that connections are all around you. Most of it is up to you and how you present yourself. This is about being interested in people, asking questions, and putting yourself "out there" and can lead to many seeds being planted.

I pray each morning that God will introduce me to the people He wants me to meet and that I will be open to meeting with them. I am a very strong extrovert so people are my passion. If you are more on the introvert side, you will have to work a bit harder at this.

What is your "connectivity quotient"?

How connected are you in your life today on a 1-10 scale?

What could you do differently today to be more connected?

Ingredient #2 is Action

Nothing happens if you do not take action. Remember the Go, do, and be seen" concept and how we need to be our own PR agents at live and virtual events. We have to start attending events to make connections.

It is important to recognize that the fortune is in the follow-up and what kind of actions you are willing to take with your connections.

What actions are you taking to connect?

How can you follow up today?

Ingredient #3 is Advantage

We all have an advantage that can be used when connecting. This is like we discussed with the power of referrals, word of mouth and the power of social media. Use your connections to increase your advantage. And be careful of the word USE. I do not mean it in a harmful way. We can "use" anything in our life to create something good or to cause harm.

We are called as Christian women entrepreneurs to use our God-given gifts for good in order to create a bridge. And really, connections are a way to be an example of how Jesus lived.

What is your advantage?

How can you use your leverage?

Ingredient #4 is Authenticity

One easy way to increase your connectivity quotient is to be real and tell your story. The people you meet want to know the real you. They want to see you. Be authentic. Talk about your journey. Find the common ground, not the differences.

If we do not connect through authentic interaction, our long term business will not thrive.

Are you sharing your real story?

Will you let people into your life?

© 2010-2013 Diane Cunningham Companies LLC

Ingredient #5 is Attitude

It is important to connect with the right attitude. We have to be attractive to attract people and much of the time this comes down to our attitude.

The truth is that if you are connecting out of guilt or responsibility then that will show up in your attitude. If I am in the wrong frame of mind, I do not want to infect others with that by going to a networking event. We are called to serve with an attitude of joy, not an attitude of imposition.

What is your attitude?

How might you need to reframe your thinking?

Ingredient #6 is Accountability

It is critical for our connections to stick for us to be accountable. This relates to many things we have already covered about mentoring and personal responsibility. Reach forward and reach back, the power of mentoring.

The bottom line is that we have to stop being vague and take ownership of our personal connections. No one else can do the work for us.

Who do you need to be accountable to?

How will you gauge your level of connecting?

Ingredient #7 is Adventure

This is the best part because connecting is an adventure. Think of it as a research project and you are studying each person that comes in your path. Learn to be a people magnet. Create joy and have some fun!

Connections are crucial for the journey as a woman of faith. We are coming to the final stages of our process and now we need to look at our time and our next steps.

What are you most excited about related to connecting?

Who is a famous person that you would love to connect with?

Handouts, Worksheets, and Templates

- Connections Quiz
- Opportunity List
- Weekly Dreaming and Ideas
- Weekly Marketing Checklist
- Weekly Review

© 2010-2013 Diane Cunningham Companies LLC

Connections Checklist

Have you completed the following?

- ☐ Connections Quiz
- ☐ Opportunity List
- ☐ Weekly Dreaming and Ideas
- ☐ Weekly Marketing Checklist
- ☐ Weekly Review

Connections Quiz

What are my relationship strengths or how do I excel in connecting?

What do I know I need to improve upon in my relationships and or connecting skills?

When meeting new people, I feel....

My mentors in my life are/have been:

I have trouble with (circle all that apply):

first impressions   follow-up   knowing what to say

reading people   relaxing   saying too much

Other_____

My other relationship questions and/or challenges are:

© 2010-2013 Diane Cunningham Companies LLC

Opportunity List

This tool is meant for you to continue expanding your awareness and "seeing" possibilities. You will not know all the answers, but this is a great time to start imagining as you try things on for size. Expand and prepare for opportunities. Allow yourself to write down the scary and crazy dreams that are part of your opportunities. My hope for you is that you have evidence of opportunities from your life. There are roads we take and roads we don't, for many different reasons. Some we don't understand for a very long time. But it is still a life lesson, and an important one.

What opportunities lie just around the bend?

What is your unique "leverage"?

Where do you see options that you didn't see before?

Why is now the right time?

What ideas are running around in your head?

What is going to stop you from trying some or all of them?

If you could make an "opportunity" happen, what would it be?

How does this relate to your life purpose?

Weekly Dream & Idea Space

© 2010-2013 Diane Cunningham Companies LLC

Weekly Marketing Checklist

Date	Networking Event, Article, Newsletter, etc

Weekly Review

What action(s) did I take during this week?

What were my wins or successes this week?

What were my challenges this week?

What have I learned about myself this week?

What is my focus for the upcoming week?

What progress have I made toward my goals? What has changed?

What three words would I use to describe this week?

© 2010-2013 Diane Cunningham Companies LLC

Chapter #9
Time

© 2010-2013 Diane Cunningham Companies LLC

What is time?

To everything there is a season, and a time to every purpose under the heaven:

A time to be born, and a time to die; a time to plant, and a time to pluck up that which is planted;

A time to kill, and a time to heal; a time to break down, and a time to build up;

A time to weep, and a time to laugh; a time to mourn, and a time to dance;

A time to cast away stones, and a time to gather stones together; a time to embrace, and a time to refrain from embracing;

A time to get, and a time to lose; a time to keep, and a time to cast away;

A time to rend, and a time to sew; a time to keep silence, and a time to speak;

A time to love, and a time to hate; a time of war, and a time of peace.

Ecclesiastes 3: 1-8

What about your time?

How can you learn to say NO and set some boundaries?

What is enough? How much is too much?

As Christian women entrepreneurs, we are trying to balance our intense desire to succeed in business with our families, friends, faith, and so much more. This topic is a tough one for us as women because we have a tendency to struggle in this area daily with the giant list of things to get done and the guilt that we feel in both directions.

What is time and how do we manage it?

According to the BusinessDictionary.com, **time management** is the systematic, priority-based structuring of time allocation and distribution among competing demands. Since time cannot be stored, and its availability can neither be increased beyond nor decreased from the 24 hours, the term 'time budgeting' is said to be the more appropriate one.

My coach Jackie Nagel once got me laughing so hard when she said time is like milk, it expires. She was right! I was trying to play with time and not see how valuable it is. I am guessing that you might do this too.

Do you try to SAVE time? Be more efficient?

I am guilty of not allowing enough time for the creative process. Being creative is not something that works well on a 50 minute slot in your calendar. What are your areas of guilt?

As we go through this chapter, be very aware of how you might need to change your schedule to create a business that works for you. We often get trapped in the mindset of time. We forget that we work for ourselves. We can easily get caught in the cycle of meeting the needs of others instead of our own.

When will you create a business that works for you?

If you work better at night, will you choose to start later in the morning?

What are your most productive hours of the day?

How will you create a schedule that fits with your own rhythm?

We seem to have a recipe for trouble related to time. We are working feverishly to succeed and trying to balance home, work, husband, kids, friends, parents, siblings, bills, church, volunteer work, exercise, etc.

I have a hand-written sign hanging from the calendar in my office that says "No More Stupid-Stuff". For me this is about bound-aries. I have to remind myself to make the right choices because frequently the first word out of my mouth is YES. I have been

© 2010-2013 Diane Cunningham Companies LLC

known to promise too much and not allow myself enough preparation and planning time. I can easily fall into a pattern of people pleasing or codependency. If a client arrives late to an appointment, it is definitely OK for me to end the session at the regular ending time. This honors my time and the time of anyone that I am in contact with. In the past, and still on occasion, this would lead me to a big pile of guilt. I have learned, and you can too, to lay down the guilt.

"Look carefully then how you walk! Live purposely not as unwise and witless, but as wise. Redeeming your time, because the days are evil." Eph.5:15-16

Obtaining wisdom is a good thing...applying wisdom is even better. So be intentional in how you walk, how you talk, and how you use your time. Live with the end in mind.

Peggy Reeves is a Christian Speaker, Writer, and Life Coach. www.peggyreeves.com

What about procrastination?

Procrastination the act of procrastinating; putting off or delaying or deferring an action to a later time.

A great book that I recommend often on this subject is called Eat That Frog by Brain Tracy. We have to learn to eat our frogs first thing in the morning, instead of avoiding them all day. This trick leads to a full day of being more productive.

How might saying NO, help you to say YES?

Managing your time is the hardest and most important lesson you can learn. Once time is gone you can't beg it or buy it back, especially with our spouse, children, parents, and friends. It is imperative to realize the VALUE of time so that you will learn to

spend it wisely and enjoy it fully. It is a gift from God each day and when we learn to see each moment that way, we will make the most of it. Leigh Ann Napier is The Happy Marriage Coach- http://leighannnapier.com

What are boundaries?

Boundaries are good for you but can often get blurred along the journey as a female entrepreneur. We become so focused on our business that we might ignore self-care and even take advantage of our family members. We might lose sight of our priorities by putting work first, day after day.

We might even have no idea what a boundary is, let alone a healthy boundary. Let's take a look together and see what changes we might need to make.

A **boundary** is a border or a limit, or the point at which something ends. Boundaries affect our relationships, our bodies, our food, our time, and much more. We need to understand our own boundaries and be aware of the boundaries of those we love.

Boundaries define us. They define what is me and what is not me. A boundary shows me where I end and someone else begins, leading me to a sense of ownership.

–Boundaries by Dr. Henry Cloud and Dr. John Townsend

It is also crucial that we understand the boundaries of our business and how to set boundaries with our clients, venders, and employees. This might include your office hours, pricing, turn-around time, return policy, or vendor contract.

In the book titled <u>Boundaries</u>, by Dr. Henry Cloud and Dr. John Townsend, they explain 4 main areas of boundary setting:

 © 2010-2013 Diane Cunningham Companies LLC

Physical boundaries help you determine who may touch you and under what circumstances.

Mental boundaries give you the freedom to have your own thoughts and opinions.

Emotional boundaries help you deal with your own emotions and disengage from the harmful, manipulative emotions of others.

Spiritual boundaries help you distinguish God's will from your own and give you renewed awe for your creator.

Boundaries provide a line of distinction for us. A clear YES and a clear NO that allows for easier decision making.

The Bible says to "guard our heart with all diligence" Boundaries are like a fence, not a wall, that helps us keep the good in and the bad out. But every fence needs a gate, both to let sin out, and good from others including God in, by receiving it. They also help us see where we end and someone else begins. Everything we say yes to, we are saying no to something else.

Vickie Minnella of Beyond Walls ~ www.thinkbeyondwalls.com

~~~~~

I set boundaries based on what works best for me energy-wise and joy-wise. If it doesn't work for me, I change it. I write, speak and coach. Morning is the ONLY time that works for me for coaching; and I can only coach about 3 mornings a week. I can take a coaching client as early as 6am, but I'm too fried to coach by 1pm. I schedule clients that way now; in the beginning, I didn't and the quality of service I delivered suffered. I can talk frequently, but morning hours are much better for me. With writing, I can do it anytime--crack of dawn, middle of the night, whenever creativity hits me. My "work" hours semi-offi-

cially are 8am-1pm Monday-Thursday, but of course I do a lot outside of those hours (like now!).

Nicole Kirksey www.foundationalgifts.com

~~~~~

Boundaries create order and focus in our lives. I've learned that setting boundaries is about being in tune with oneself enough to say No and mean it. One thing that I have learned to do over the last few years is to not answer my phone. Now for some of you this might sound crazy. For me, this is an important boundary. I spend most of my days on the phone with coaching and groups. I can't know if a call will be short or long if I answer it. And often I need more information prior to talking to someone by phone. So I do not answer. That is a boundary.

What boundaries do you need to set today?

We can struggle with boundaries as we grow our business from the ground up and become "codependent" with our need for certain clients or customers. This is often called putting all of your "eggs in one basket". I have experienced this personally with relying on certain contracts to meet my financial projections and then that contract falling through or being terminated.

What is codependency?

Codependency is when a relationship creates a mutual need. It becomes the dependence of two people, groups, or organisms on each other. Now we all have mutual need with each other and especially as a member of a family, team, marriage, or staff. It can become harmful when it takes on an addictive nature or reinforces mutually harmful behavior patterns.

© 2010-2013 Diane Cunningham Companies LLC

Many women entrepreneurs are in the midst of unhealthy relationships with a business partner, team member, franchise partner, mentor, or joint venture partner but feel they cannot afford to terminate the toxic relationship due to the financial implications.

What about working from a home office?

One big challenge for many female entrepreneurs is working from a home office. This brings in a whole other set of challenges related to work space, kids, pets, and interruptions. When your office is just down the hall, you can find yourself drifting back in there at times that you might not have wanted to. The real truth is that when we are passionate about our business, it can take on an addictive nature. When we are in our start-up years trying to keep our businesses afloat and meet the demands of growth, we might be working again into the wee hours of the night.

We don't have any less time than that wise woman described in Proverbs 31, and we have all kinds of conveniences to make our lives easier, but somehow most of us get less done. If you really want to be a wise steward of your time, you need to dedicate a time and a space in your life for your passions and turn off the distractions. Check e-mail once a day, turn off the TV, and focus on the activities that really matter in building your business.
Karen Palmer www.worryfreemom.com

Without boundaries, relationships become damaged and tangled. This can lead to "passive-aggressive" behavior, which is really just a sneaky way to be angry. This is not attractive to our business and certainly not attractive in our personal life. We have to learn how to become assertive, not aggressive or passive.

Assertiveness and the 4 Basic Communication Styles

Passive: is a style in which individuals have developed a pattern of avoiding expressing their opinions or feelings, protecting their rights, and identifying and meeting their needs. Passive communication is usually born of low self-esteem.

Aggressive: is a style in which individuals express their feelings and opinions and advocate for their needs in a way that violates the rights of others. Thus, aggressive communicators are verbally and/or physically abusive. Aggressive communication is born of low self-esteem (often caused by past physical and/or emotional abuse), unhealed emotional wounds, and feelings of powerlessness.

Passive-Aggressive: is a style in which individuals appear passive on the surface but are really acting out anger in subtle, indirect, or behind the scenes way. People who develop a pattern of passive-aggressive communication usually feel powerless, stuck, and resentful- in other words, they feel incapable of dealing directly with the object of their resentment.

Assertive: is a style in which individuals clearly state their opinions and feelings, and firmly advocate for their rights and needs without violating the rights of others. Assertive communication is born of high self-esteem. These individuals value themselves, their time, and their emotional, spiritual, and physical needs and are strong advocates for themselves while being very respectful of the rights of others.

Learning to identify our own communication style can be a key factor is our success plan. Watch how you respond to certain people and in certain situations. Learn and grow from each interaction. Help your clients, customers, and colleagues to communicate assertively by being a role model.

© 2010-2013 Diane Cunningham Companies LLC

It is important that we teach our team, clients, and colleagues how to set boundaries and how to be assertive too by the way we interact. Set the example and others will learn from you.

Learning to set Boundaries

I am still trying to figure out this "boundary thing". I can see twice this past week when I said yes and I should have said no. Tammy Kniffen, CEO of the Global Alliance of Special Needs Support

Setting boundaries is difficult for me. I worry more about making others happy and many times do not stay true to myself and my purpose. I bounce feelings off of my husband-he keeps me grounded.

Melinda Keeling from www.PiggiesandPaws.com

"Good boundary behavior" might involve:

- Leaving the office at a certain time each day, in spite of the work you still have to do
- Closing your office door in order to complete a project or deadline
- Referring clients to a competitor if they do not fit into your niche and they take you back to who you used to be

"Bad boundary behavior" might involve:

- Working all week during the day, and then again each evening and all weekend.

- Answering all texts, phone calls, and emails no matter what the time and no matter who you are with
- Giving away your time, above what you have been contracted for, in order to not upset or lose a client, and then not billing the client for the time

Learning to say NO!

No is a complete sentence. No. See, I just used it.

Say No and say it a lot. This is something that takes years of practice, but we can start today. I have been known to give my coaching clients the homework assignment of "saying no" to as many things or people as possible. This causes quite a stir and leads to giant leaps in awareness into their own struggle.

We might have to just give ourselves permission to say NO. We are allowed to say NO. We are allowed to not have a valid reason. We have the authority and can veto something that is in process. As the saying goes, when we close the door, it makes room for us to go toward the open window.

Important Facts about No

No is allowed and acceptable.

No is not NEVER.

No is not MAYBE.

No is not about being bribed.

No is not a SIN.

© 2010-2013 Diane Cunningham Companies LLC

No does not mean you will lose business. Saying NO might be what you need to do to increase your business.

The power of YES

What happens when you say YES? I have experienced the power and miracles of saying YES.

YES allows for more YES.

YES provides room for new opportunities.

YES helps NO come with more clarity in other places.

YES takes the power away from the FEAR.

Recently I found a small gift sized book with the striking title of <u>HELL YES!</u> Written by Elizabeth Cogswell Baskin. I sat in the book store and read this entire little book in about 10 minutes. But I made the choice to buy it anyway. I have it sitting on the top shelf in my office on display with the title facing out as a visual reminder. The entire book basically says the following. If you can't say Hell Yes, then it should be a Hell No. We have no time to waste and if it is something that you feel like you need to think about, consider, or ponder over, then it really might fit into the hell no category. Fabulous message and something we can so easily drift away from.

As the amazing and visionary women that we are, it really comes down to not being wishy-washy. As a well know scripture says, Let your Yes be Yes, and your No be No. Good advice and practical wisdom for all of us to use.

What am I saying YES to?

You might then ask yourself this question: If I say YES, what am I saying YES TO?

Say Yes to FREE time and Self Care.

Say Yes to getting Help.

Say Yes to assertive communication.

Say Yes to setting healthy boundaries.

Say Yes to your own vision and dream.

Choices

As a female entrepreneur, we have so many boundaries to set and so many choices to make each day. We can struggle with boundaries because of our drive for success and our struggle to make our business viable. I have struggled a great deal with setting boundaries around my work time and learning to say NO. This can take a huge toil on our relationships. We want to succeed so much that we are willing to work at a fevered pitch. When a potential client calls or emails, we feel compelled to say YES, take the call, make the appointment. This is a hard lesson to learn. We have to get comfortable with putting people into our schedule and not rearranging everything to meet their last minute deadline or urgent request.

The other boundary issue is that we tend to be so IN our business, doing what we do best that we don't look AT our business with a long range vision and plan. This is when we can end up realizing that we have an event next week and have no flyers, posters, etc. This is when we become that dreaded person who is frantically asking for last minute help in a panic. This goes back

 © 2010-2013 Diane Cunningham Companies LLC

to the message about strategic planning in the marketing module.

This is a struggle for me. I try to set aside time for work, as well as time for family. The nature of what I do to help P&P on FB means that there are quiet times, and then there are other times where I can't seem to take a breath without someone else needing help, guidance, support.

Melanie Stofka from www.PiggiesandPaws.com

No matter how crazy my week seems to get, I always start my day by spending the first half hour with our Lord. I pour a cup of coffee and read the bible. After I review my calendar, and start my day. Heather Potvin, Hharpp Accounting Services www.hharpp.com

We live with an amazing opportunity to make choices, with our free will. I am not sure about you, but sometimes I forget this. I have to talk to myself and say out loud, "I have a choice."

The following questions help me in this process of choosing.

What is the best choice for me?

What might happen if I make the wrong choice?

What is the worst case scenario?

How will this choice affect my business in 30 days?

How will this choice affect my business one year from now?

Does this move me closer or farther away from my vision?

Does this choice reflect my core values?

Does this choice line up with my written mission statement?

What is Self-Care?

Self care is personal health maintenance. It is any activity of an individual, family or community, with the intention of improving or restoring health, or treating or preventing disease.

Self care includes all health decisions people (as individuals or consumers) make for themselves and their families to get and stay physically and mentally fit. Self care is exercising to maintain physical fitness and good mental health. It is also eating well, self-medicating, practicing good hygiene and avoiding health hazards such as smoking.

Let's look at how Deborah White, from A Matter of Balance uses a simple tool to create space in her day.

One Friday I was sitting in my office here in my home and I had this surprising thought that I had gone the entire week without once doing anything for my own self care. You know things like take a bubble bath or eat a piece of chocolate with a cup of coffee or take a few minutes to cross stitch. I truly was happy all week long but I realized in that moment something was missing in my week and I knew some self care was it. Since this is the business that I am in, time management, where I help women create open spaces for free time, I thought it pretty funny that I had missed the mark myself and began to chuckle out loud. I said, "ok that's it I need to plug into my calendar some me time."

At that moment I blocked off an hour on the following Monday and called it "White Space" as my last name is White. I didn't write what I would do in that hour, but I thought that I would somehow know what to do when it came. After all how would I know what would fill up the self care cup three days from today? So, about 5 minutes before that hour, I sat quiet and asked myself what I would love to have happen that would be wonderful that I could create for the next hour that I had blocked

© 2010-2013 Diane Cunningham Companies LLC

off for myself. I thought you know I would love to go for a walk because it was a warm day, I also thought to take my two dogs with me and I also thought a cup of hazelnut coffee and a piece of chocolate would be great as I read a book for the last 20 minutes of my great hour. Wow, I thought how profound it was that I knew exactly what I needed in that moment and I had one solid hour to do it in. It felt fantastic. I wouldn't have known on Friday when I was making this up for myself but I sure knew what it was on Monday. Simple enough.... I set the time, called it White Space, and asked myself what I would love to do just 5 minutes before I started doing what would make my heart sing. I want to tell you that I felt wonderful and had an incredible amount of energy at the end of the hour that really surprised me.

It has been over a year that I have continued to use this White Space system for myself and my clients in my Life Coaching business. I am always pleasantly surprised every time by the outcome. So, right now block off some time and enjoy some White Space for yourself!

www.amatterofbalancecoaching.com

Exercise for Self-Care

Exercise and eating right is a key factor for women entrepreneurs. I know that my time to walk and run needs to be a non-negotiable. In fact, I actually get some of my most creative entrepreneurial ideas when I am out exercising.

I try to exercise three to four times a week - sometimes it's only once. Very rarely do I entirely miss a week. I try to make good food choices, but I'm not rigorous about it. Personal health is definitely an area that I need to improve. I'm taking action on it, but I'm not where I want or need to be yet.

Lynda-Ross Vega from www.aciforentrepreneurs.com

What boundaries do you need to set? Or re-set?

What do you need to say No to, so that you can Say YES?

What do you need to do for self-care?

Priorities and Time

What do you value? This is reflected in our priorities and the use of our time.

The things we value gain our highest priority with a sense of urgency or priority treatment. This means rearranging our schedule and often times our budget. As female entrepreneurs, we learn to reevaluate often and change plans as needed.

Absolutely do not answer the phone, hired a cleaning lady, and know my best time of day is first thing in the morning. I get my kids off to school, workout because that is good for me, and then block the next five hours, until it's time to get the kids again. That's the routine at least four days a week, but I reserve Friday to be "free choice" day. If I've accomplished a lot during the week, then Friday can be a play day, lunch with friends, shop etc. If I need to work, then I forego the workout and get work done by lunch. That way I can still be fresh for the weekend.

Allison Rouse Johnson from www.resurrectedgirl.com

© 2010-2013 Diane Cunningham Companies LLC

Key Tools for our Time and Productivity:

- Using a master planner or calendar system that works for you
- Time mapping
- Having a weekly time plan and certain days for certain tasks
- Delegating things that we do not need to do
- Office hours
- Using the timer system

I believe I have my priorities straight. God first, family second (I also love my neighbor!), business/work last. I also believe that self-care is essential to all, so that's way up on my list.

Deni Carruth from www.masterkeyscoaching.com

I try to have set office hours and have worked harder at protecting my evenings and weekends so I can spend time with my husband and family. This is new for me because I was not able to do that when my son was young and I was a single mom. Also, being remarried now I am trying to build in couple's times with my husband.

Kristi Olson from www.purposereleased.com

So you can see that there are many things for us to learn related to boundaries and our business. The more you practice this, the better you will become and it will have a direct affect on your business growth.

Handouts, Worksheets, and Templates

- Stop, Start, Continue Chart
- Time Review
- Areas that I need to work on

Are you ready to look at your time and create a new plan?
Go to www.nacwe.org/ToolkitResources to get your own set of
the 47 templates by using the coupon code: success

© 2010-2013 Diane Cunningham Companies LLC

Stop-Start-Continue Chart

This tool is to help you see what you are doing and not doing.
What do you need to continue doing? My hope for you is that you
will see exactly what you know to be true and have been afraid
to say out loud. My prayer for you is that you will do something
about it!

Stop	Start	Continue

Time Review

This tool is to help you really see your time and decide if it is matching up with your priorities. We often think we are living by this, but we all suffer from the disease of "vagueness" and it often shows itself in our time. My hope for you is that you will be aware of the choices you are making with your time. There is only so much of it each day...and you get to choose how you spend it. What will you choose?

Time: How are you spending it?

There are 168 hours in a week.

You spend about....

56 hours sleeping

40 hours working

21 hours eating (an hour for each meal)

Total = 117

You now have 51 hours each week to spend.

How do you want to spend that time?

© 2010-2013 Diane Cunningham Companies LLC

Areas that I need to work on:

Problem	Strategy	Action Step

Time Checklist

Have you completed the following?

- ☐   Stop- Start-Continue Chart
- ☐   Time Review
- ☐   Weekly Dreaming and Ideas
- ☐   Weekly Marketing Checklist
- ☐   Weekly Review

© 2010-2013 Diane Cunningham Companies LLC

Weekly Dream & Idea Space

Weekly Marketing Checklist

Date	Networking Event, Article, Newsletter, etc

© 2010-2013 Diane Cunningham Companies LLC

Weekly Review

What action(s) did I take during this week?

What were my wins or successes this week?

What were my challenges this week?

What have I learned about myself this week?

What is my focus for the upcoming week?

What progress have I made toward my goals? What has changed?

What three words would I use to describe this week?

© 2010-2013 Diane Cunningham Companies LLC

Chapter #10
Next Steps

© 2010-2013 Diane Cunningham Companies LLC

What are your next steps?

For I know the plans I have for you says the Lord, plans to prosper you and not to harm you. Jeremiah 29:11

What are your next steps?

Where are you going and how will you get there?

What plans have you implemented during our time together?

We are always going to have more to do. There will always be a next step to take. We have plenty more to learn.

As a Christian woman and an entrepreneur, you have been given a gift from God. This last chapter is all about ongoing learning. I like to say the "we have much to learn and much to teach".

I love to learn and truly could be a perpetual student. The world is fascinating to me and I find inspiration in almost every direction. How people can say they are "bored" is a mystery to me. As a female entrepreneur, when we have a rare moment in time, you will often find us out learning about our trade or business. We are a learning bunch and we really don't like to let much grass grow under us! We keep moving and we tend to move fast.

What is your class schedule or syllabus?

A syllabus is an outline or a summary of the main points of a text, lecture, or course of study.

The fabulous part about our next steps and our ongoing learning is that we can create our own syllabus or agenda. Remember all of those required classes we had in school? Now we can put ourselves back into the classes of our choosing. This makes so much sense to the female entrepreneur as we develop into each phase of learning. The things I am ready to learn now are much different than 2 years ago or 5 years ago when I first launched my business.

Let me give you an example from both my business and my personal life. If we looked at my class schedule or syllabus for 2013 it would include the following:

- Move to a new city
- Marketing
- Creating info-products
- Self-publish a book
- Record a video coaching series
- Zumba
- Running/walking
- Weight Loss
- Relationships and Dating
- Faith

We have so much to learn each day. In fact, if we really paid attention, at the end of each day we could create a very nice article called "Lessons I learned Today".

Do you look at the world through learning glasses?

Where do you find inspiration to keep moving forward?

What have you already experienced as you became an entrepreneur?

What have I learned already?

© 2010-2013 Diane Cunningham Companies LLC

Sometimes we forget how much we really have learned along the way, until we look back. I see learning as a big part of staying inspired and motivated. As I gather new information, my brain seems to light up. This is a big part of the entrepreneur journey as we are trailblazers and rebels.

How do I choose my next steps?

I love finding inspiration and ideas in the most bizarre places. I can get inspired from a trip to Walmart. I can learn something new from reading what my Facebook connections add to their wall. I can get a great idea by hearing someone talking at Starbucks when I am getting my morning coffee. I can be inspired by a photograph or a gadget. I can get ideas from a person, a place, or a thing.

My point is that we all have the same opportunities and daily repetitive tasks to complete. But what if you look at them through the eyes of your business and with a new set of glasses? What if you opened up your mind to some new directions? What if we claim the world as our giant classroom? What if we looked at the world with "inspired eyes"?

"Inspired Eyes" allow you to use your creativity to its full capacity. One of the great joys of being an entrepreneur is the creative spirit and lack of walls holding you back. You are the boss and you set the tone.

As we consider different opportunities for learning, it is important to know how we learn best. We each have our own unique learning style. This learning style is vital in how you can best take the knowledge and utilize it in a meaningful way.

How do you learn best?

What is your learning style?

Let's look at all of the ways you can keep taking the next step.

Seminars and Workshops

Continual learning is huge for me. I personally attend workshops and retreats continually and read constantly. I also offer learning opportunities for all the women in my business. Jennifer Carrillo Thomas from Piggies and Paws

Do you attend workshops?

What retreat or seminars have you attended this year?

Are you attending any lunch and learn programs?

Have you connected to your local Small Business Development Center?

What about the amazing wide variety of tele-courses and seminars that are offered on the internet?

I admit that much of my entrepreneurial journey has been on the phone. I have attended phenomenal free calls that changed the course of my business. I have invested in myself with free and paid training and coaching.

I attend any seminar that is offered in my area that could be a good learning opportunity and networking venue.

A few years ago, I asked a colleague who is many years wiser than myself the following question when we met for lunch: "Knowing what you know now…If you were me, what advice would you give me?" She said this: "The best thing I ever did was to continue to invest in myself. I attended all of the trainings and the seminars that I could. I paid for further education. Keep investing in your-

© 2010-2013 Diane Cunningham Companies LLC

self and you will continue to be on the cutting edge of your field." I have taken her advice.

What about you? What events have you attended this year? What events do you want to get on your calendar today?

Now you might be dealing with these thoughts:

- "I don't have the money for more training."
- "How will I get the time to attend these trainings?
- "Will this training increase my bottom line?
- "How will my family deal with me being away to attend the training?"

I choose each year, to set aside money that I will use to add another training to my tool belt. I love how this choice has opened new doors for me and created new revenue streams. It has also added new connections for referrals and ongoing personal development.

Certifications and Trainings

How about additional certifications and training?

Do you need to add some new skills?

There are home study courses, certification programs, self-paced modules. There are also live events for all fields that are crucial for the female entrepreneur to attend for numerous reasons.

A photographer friend of mine just spent one week at Photography School. She said what she learned was life-changing, but the key ingredient that made it worthwhile was the new friendships. I agree!

Often the best learning is done on the lunch break with a small group or at the table during a class assignment. It could be a mastermind group that is created from a group of women you connect with at the event. Be open and willing to ask for what you need. I met with a group of women faithfully each month after we met an event in 2009 and am still in contact with them now.

Books and Magazines

Are you staying up to date on the books and magazines that your clients are reading? Are you willing to invest in the reading material that your competition might be seeing in order to stay fresh?

I am a book-aholic and enjoy reading a great deal. At any given time, you might laugh when you see me reading 3 or 4 books, a few ebooks I have downloaded, and even some magazines for fun. In fact, I might be one of the few people in my age group that still has the daily newspaper delivered and reads it each morning. On my home bookshelf, which could really be turned into a small library at some point, you would find a diet section, a running section, a marketing section, self-help, psychology, Christianity and much more. I love books and can really get myself into a heap of trouble at the book store.

I want to have the information that I need and be ready to share it with others or suggest the correct book for the situation or challenge they are working on. Many people have asked me over the last few years how I am able to read so much. Well here is my secret. I read in the bathtub almost every night. Yes the secret is out. This is how I have learned most of what I know. I have been teased for taking highlighters and even a 3 ring binder with me to the tub. It sounds so funny to write this. But this is my 20-30 minutes of uninterrupted time. I am not talking, leading,

 © 2010-2013 Diane Cunningham Companies LLC

coaching, or marketing. It is just me reading. So where can you squeeze in some time to read? Is it on the elliptical? It is on your lunch hour? When waiting for the kids? Or maybe you want to start reading in the tub?

Internet and all Social Media

I have learned so much through the amazing resource that we have for FREE...the World Wide Web. Are you getting out and about virtually to see what your clients are talking about? You don't have to eavesdrop or even leave your office. They are speaking, connecting, joining, and sharing right in front of you. In fact, they are talking about you and your business. Give them a place to do that. Make it easy for them!

With social media, such as Facebook and Twitter, you have a world of learning at your fingertips through video, webinars, and more.

This has changed the playing field for us as female entrepreneurs and connected us to people that we never could have met.

More and more, we are a virtual society. And whether you are connecting with clients around the world or around your city, it is crucial. In fact, I would say it is non-negotiable.

Having a business page on Facebook for your hair salon or bakery, helps your clients to see you and be a part of your life. It allows them room to share a testimony is an easy way. You might show before and after photos of your work, or photos of your clients in action. It provides a place for others to see your work and get a glimpse into the atmosphere at your business. That is priceless marketing!!

Journaling and Self-Reflection

What about journaling and self-reflection? I have been a journal kind of girl since high school. It looks different now than it did then, but it is still a valuable tool for me.

It is important for me to take a step back and check in with myself. I need to see where I am emotionally as I build my business and to focus in on my dream. Reading back through my journals helps me to see how far I have come and the successes I have had.

It is here in the self-reflection that I can look at myself and do personal reflection. I can get really honest. I can share my thoughts and feelings.

I know that some of you may have never journaled before and I want to challenge you to give it a try. Don't knock it until you try it. Maybe it is just what you need.

There are many ways to journal:

Coffee Shop Journaling: I take my journal and grab a cup of coffee and just write. I let the words pour out. It might be bullet points or just stream of consciousness. I often end the journal entry with a letter. Sometimes this is a letter to myself and other times it is a letter to God.

Success Log Journaling: This technique I started when I was using the Get Clients Now 28 Day marketing system. At the end of each day, I log 2 entries into my small spiral notebook. The page has the date and then 2 sections Successes of Today and Things I Could Do Better Tomorrow. I take the judgment out of it and really just try to observe myself. I use a bullet point system.

Computer Journaling or a Blog: Many people use their blog as a sort of journal. It can be a place for you to be as honest as

 © 2010-2013 Diane Cunningham Companies LLC

you want to be. Or you could just use a word document and type a journal entry.

Facebook: In many ways, my Facebook page becomes my on-line journal as I share my life with my friends and the world.

I encourage you to journal and see what happens.

Visual and Hands-On Learning

Many entrepreneurs love to get busy and DIVE IN with hands-on learning. We like to try things and see how they might work for us. Some of us might be guilty of not reading the instruction manual or even asking enough questions because we are so ready to take ACTION and get started.

We can learn so much from being face to face with another female entrepreneur to "SEE" how she does it.

The best ways for me are visual, viewing a live presentation, a demonstration, or a video. Don't just tell me things show me. Let me feel, touch & find out for myself.

Margie Gaitan from Mary Kay

I learn from experience! I learn from both my own mistakes and from either watching what others do or hearing from them on their tips of what NOT to do.

Mary Pool from www.PiggiesandPaws.com

I learn by doing and I am a very hands on learner. I learn from others stories as well as my own life.

Rhoda Baty from www.lifecoachingwithrhoda.com

Going back to College?

Do you need more traditional schooling? There is so much to learn on a college campus and we don't want to count this out of our discussion. I wouldn't trade my college years for anything. I also loved my years in graduate school going to night classes and learning about counseling theories.

I had the great honor of being in the business incubator program from April of 2009 to July of 2010 at our local college. This provided me with an office in the business college right next door to the Entrepreneurial studies department. I loved being close to the Small Business Development Center and having access to the professors just down the hall. We often learn so much from the environment around us.

Don't be afraid of adding additional schooling to your tool-belt. College campuses are also a great place to network. Plus many schools now offer online programs that are often evening courses.

The A-Ha moments or Life Lessons Learning

So much of my entrepreneur journey has been learned in just doing things the wrong way or through a life lesson. We have so much knowledge tucked away from just living LIFE, that we can tap into on a daily basis. I am stubborn and often have to do things MY way and then fall on my face. This is just part of the process. I accept it now. I have learned to embrace it and use all of my life as part of the entrepreneurial adventure. My business is an integral part of my life and each day has tasks to master and projects to complete....basically lessons to learn. I just as easily might meet my next client while getting my nails done, as I could at a networking event.

© 2010-2013 Diane Cunningham Companies LLC

Last week, I had a great example of this. I was leading a tele-class training which I have done hundreds of time. I have done all of these calls on a cell phone for 4 years and only had a few problems to speak of. Well, last week's call was a little dose of reality as my phone was cut off not once, but 4 times on the call. So here I am, the coach, having to call back in to get reconnected to the group. Luckily each time, the group was still there waiting for me. We kept moving right along and I tried to just make the situation a good learning opportunity for all. The show must go on, right?

What have you learned by going through the fire?

What are some of your recent A-ha moments?

How have you used a recent learning opportunity to add something or change your business?

Consistent Action
Finding the Time, and the Right Combination

So how are you going to make the time to learn?

How much is enough?

What is best combination of learning and action?

Each of us will have to make wise choices. I read at night, in the bath tub. Just like many things along the entrepreneurial path, there will be sacrifices to be made. There is a time and a place for learning and then a time to stop learning and start doing. Sometimes I see women who are perpetually training and never moving to the action phase. They can be found on every FREE call and almost addicted to the information gathering. This can be a serious stumbling block. Most of the time, we just need to get busy DOING. We know enough. It is time to ACT.

There are also financial implications of the learning we need to do. We have to watch our spending and not go overboard in the learning and training department.

I try to attend one or two retreats a year just for the networking and to listen to what people think the hot topics are. I'm a skim reader, looking for articles that interest me. I watch for new books and select those I'll read based on reviews and if the topic is intriguing. Michelle Martin www.c3forwomen.com

Information Overload

One thing that is not often talked about, but is a challenge for each of us is **information overload**. This is a term popularized by Alvin Toffler that refers to the difficulty a person can have understanding an issue and making decisions that can be caused by the presence of too much information. This term was created before we even added the internet and texting and all other realms into the sensory mix. We can become so overwhelmed that it can paralyze us into NO action.

I'm very selective. It's too easy to get overwhelmed with all of the info available about what you should be doing to grow your business. I try to find a few voices that make sense to me and follow them. Lynda Ross Vega

There are not enough hours in the day to read everything, experience everything that I want to learn.

Melanie Stofka from www.piggiesandpaws.com

We each need to be selective and purposeful in our learning. Turn the gadgets off as needed. Create a boundary around certain information products. Give yourself a time limit to make

© 2010-2013 Diane Cunningham Companies LLC

certain decisions that could otherwise go unmade.   Do not allow information overload to create chaos in your brain.

Handouts, Worksheets, and Templates

- Year in Review
- Celebrations

Next Steps Checklist

Have you completed the following?

- ☐   Year in Review
- ☐   Celebrations
- ☐   Weekly Dreaming and Ideas
- ☐   Weekly Marketing Checklist
- ☐   Weekly Review

© 2010-2013 Diane Cunningham Companies LLC

Year in Review

This tool is to help you look back on the year and reflect. It is important to schedule time to be alone so that you can write and think. Consider all that you have experienced this year. Look over your Inspired Business Toolkit and re-read all of your entries. My hope for you is that you will see how much you have learned this year and how you have evolved.

As I look over this past year, the feelings that come to mind are:

If I was writing a book about my life, what would the title of this chapter be, and what would be the title of the book?

What BIG lessons did I learn this year?

What would I do differently, if I could?

Who were the key players on my support team this year?

How am I different today, than I was a year ago?

Celebrations

This tool is to help you celebrate and honor the journey. Life and business are filled with celebrations and yet we lose the real meaning as we get busy throughout the year. Stop long enough to celebrate.

My hope for you is that you will celebrate your faith, your self, your family, your friends, your mission, and your purpose. My prayer is that you are a walking testimony.

I celebrate...

I celebrate...

I celebrate...

I celebrate...

I celebrate...

I celebrate...

I celebrate...

© 2010-2013 Diane Cunningham Companies LLC

Weekly Dream & Idea Space

Weekly Marketing Checklist

Date	Networking Event, Article, Newsletter, etc

© 2010-2013 Diane Cunningham Companies LLC

Weekly Review

What action(s) did I take during this week?

What were my wins or successes this week?

What were my challenges this week?

What have I learned about myself this week?

What is my focus for the upcoming week?

What progress have I made toward my goals? What has changed?

What three words would I use to describe this week?

© 2010-2013 Diane Cunningham Companies LLC

Chapter #11

Conclusion

© 2010-2013 Diane Cunningham Companies LLC

In Closing...

This book is about you and about me. I hope you feel inspired and willing to try new things. My hope is that you have investigated the concepts in this book by taking action. I pray that your views are shifted and that you can see bigger possibilities for yourself in the world.

My goal is to do all that I can to help you with the God-given gift of a business.

Do all that can with what you have.

Get help.

Invest in yourself.

Be willing to fail.

Watch for open doors and closed doors.

Embrace what you learn about yourself and how to run your business so it works for you.

Above all us, know that God is your boss, and He has a plan!

With love,

Diane

© 2010-2013 Diane Cunningham Companies LLC

Entrepreneur Success Rolo-dex

Article	www.ezinearticles.com
Assessments	www.assessmentgenerator.com
	www.surveymonkey.com
	www.micropoll.com
Audio	www.audioacrobat.com
Blog	www.wordpress.com
Book Publishing	www.lulu.com
	www.vervante.com
	www.minibuk.com
Business Cards	www.vistaprint.com
Business Information	www.businessdictionary.com
Coaching	www.dianecunningham.com
	www.nacwe.org
Conference Calls	www.freeconferencecall.com
	www.freeconferencepro.com
	www.freeconferencecalling.com
Copyright, LLC, Trademark	www.legalzoom.com
Document Sharing	www.showdocument.com
Domain	www.godaddy.com
Email Auto-responders	www.aweber.com
	www.premiumwebcart.com
	www.1shoppingcart.com
Email Marketing	www.constantcontact.com
	www.gladhandle.com
	www.mailchimp.com
	www.icontact.com
	www.getresponse.com
Forum	www.activeboard.com
Fulfillment Services	www.vervante.com

Graphic and Logo Design	www.deeprootedmarketing.com
	Christine Dupre cedupre@msn.com
Marketing Training	www.nacwe.org
Money	www.paypal.com
Radio-online	www.blogtalkradio.com
Social Networking	www.facebook.com
	www.twitter.com
	www.ping.fm
Speaker Training	www.classervices.com
	www.toastmasters.org
Video Camera	www.theflip.com
Virtual Assistant	www.virtuallysolvednow.com
	www.alyssaavant.com
	www.deeprootedmarketing.com
Website Design	www.alyssaavant.com
	www.virtuallysolvednow.com

© 2010-2013 Diane Cunningham Companies LLC

About Diane Cunningham

Diane Cunningham, M.Ed. is the President and Founder of the *National Association of Christian Women Entrepreneurs®,* a global association for women to connect, create, and collaborate. NACWE offers training, conferences, networking, and business strategies. NACWE was launched in May 2010 and has been building and expanding since that time with members throughout the United States and Canada.

Since 2005, Diane has worked under the DianeCunningham.com umbrella as a coach, speaker, facilitator, and entrepreneur. She is a "business therapist", plane crash survivor, author, consultant, marathon runner, and fun friend.

Diane loves to teach women, men and companies how to Act Fast Now with marketing online and offline through the power of social media and authentic connections. She is often called "the head cheerleader" of NACWE and she proudly wears that title.

Her training and background is in the mental health field. She worked for many years in a hospital Employee Assistance Program. Prior to that she spent time working with domestic violence and addictions. She has a Masters Degree in Education (Guidance and Counseling) from Whitworth College in Spokane, Washington and a Bachelors Degree from the same school in Interpersonal Communications. She is also a Certified Mastermind Executive Coach.

Diane is the author of "Dear Female Entrepreneur, My Friend" and the co-author of "Inspired Women Succeed" along with Jo

Ann Fore.

She currently lives in Texas, but has also lived in California and Washington state. She has served as the Regional Advocate for the Small Business Development Center for North Texas. In 2010, she was named as one of the Top 20 Under 40 emerging leaders in Wichita Falls, Texas. She is active in her church, local community events, and non-profit organizations that fit with her life mission.

Diane loves people, shopping, Starbucks, reading, and spending time with friends. She has run 4 marathons with the Leukemia & Lymphoma Society's Team in Training program and loves to go to zumba classes.

Diane's mission is this: "My mission is to inspire women to dream big, catch on fire, and change the world."

Find out more about NACWE and why 165 women joined in the first year at www.nacwe.org. Connect with Diane at www.face-book.com/DianeCunningham for fun updates, silly videos, lively conversation and great ACT FAST NOW business mentoring." Email her at diane@dianecunningham.com.

Are you ready to join our sisterhood today?   Go here now and get connected....we can't wait to meet you! Become a member: nacwe.org/nacwe-membership/

© 2010-2013 Diane Cunningham Companies LLC

Connect with Diane

www.facebook.com/DianeCunningham

www.facebook.com/NACWE

www.twitter.com/DianeCunningham

www.YouTube.com/LifeCoachDiane or www.InspiredWomenTv.com

www.LinkedIn.com/DianeCunninghamCompanies

Get my Free Training program: www.nacwe.org/freetraining

Did you get your FREE GIFTS yet? Go to www.nacwe.org/ToolkitResources to get the Launch Plan, the Marketing Circle and all of the 47 templates. Use the coupon code: success

© 2010-2013 Diane Cunningham Companies LLC

Join our NACWE family!

Are you a woman that has the dream of starting a business?

Or a woman who has been successful in business but lacking support with a group of like-minded friends?

Are you a Christian entrepreneur tired of being alone with your standards, ethics and values?

We know how you feel....

- Are you wondering where to begin?
- Fearful of asking for the sale?
- Do you struggle with social media?
- Are you totally overwhelmed with your list of to-do's?
- Struggling to figure out if you need to hire help and who to hire?
- Feeling isolated as you work alone or as the boss of a small group?

Or you might be...

- Undercharging for your services
- Overwhelmed by technology
- Afraid of being "salesy"
- Know you need a better system, but have no idea what that means

You have found the right place!

At NACWE, we "get it" and we "get you"! We get you because we are YOU!

The National Association of Christian Women Entrepreneurs was born out of a passion to connect women who are ready to create, collaborate, and contribute to changing the world. We gather people and ideas together through online content, tele-courses, individual/group coaching and retreats. Our desire is to unite under a common goal of helping one another to succeed and thrive in business. We are blessed to share in a common faith in Jesus Christ and yet know that we might each choose to worship in a different way.

Get **connected** to Christian Women Entrepreneurs throughout the United States and Canada for networking, business building, and prayer support

Start **creating** new ideas, plans, programs and products with valuable monthly training calls and webinars

Begin **collaborating** with women who can walk beside you on the journey with love and not competition

Visit us at www.nacwe.org to get started with your membership today!

© 2010-2013 Diane Cunningham Companies LLC

Invite Diane to Speak

Inspiring Heart Based Business Women To Infinite Success

Diane Cunningham is a gifted communicator who offers inspiration, motivation, and encouragement to all those who come into her path. Her genuine transparency comes through in the insightful examples she gives her audiences as she helps them to create a life filled with passion and purpose. She loves to provide inspiration strategies for your business group, weekend gathering, or corporate retreat.

As a Speaker, Diane facilitates interactive discussions, along with providing useful and thought-provoking information for seminars, networking events, and women's retreats in the church and corporate realm. She is also available for corporate training events and keynotes.

"Diane Cunningham is an engaging, enlightening, speaker. Her powerful, heartfelt message is full of substance, easily remembered and when implemented, inspires women to a higher level of success. It is with the greatest of confidence that I recommend Diane Cunningham."

– Julie Ziglar Norman

Founder of Ziglar Women, Guideposts Author, International Inspirational Speaker www.ZiglarWomen.com

Diane speaks to groups of:

- Christian Women in Business
- Entrepreneurs
- Chamber of Commerce members
- Direct Sales Companies

Most Requested Presentations:

- Inspired Business Secrets: Marketing Tools to Generate Leads, Increase Reveune, and Build a Thriving Community!
- Act Fast Now: Jumpstart Your Business with the A.C.T.I.O.N. Formula for Success
- Learn How to Catapult Your Business with Heart Based Communities

Contact Diane at diane@dianecunningham.com or visit http://nacwe.org/speaking/ to discuss the ideal program for your next event.

Diane would love to share with your group, team, company, or church. Go to www.nacwe.org/speaking or email her at diane@dianecunningham.com to discuss your needs for your next virtual or live event.

© 2010-2013 Diane Cunningham Companies LLC

Coaching with Diane Cunningham

- Do you need more clients so you can get into higher profits and help your family?
- Are you sick and tired of lying awake at night feeling overwhelmed and like you are never going to "arrive"?
- Are you ready to finally use your God-given gifts and strengths to make more money and start supporting the causes you are passionate about?
- Do you need accountability, guidance, and tough love to stop HIDING OUT and really build a business empire?

In addition to the membership options at the National Association of Christian Women Entreperneurs, Diane coaches a select number of clients each year privately and in small mastermind groups.

She provides coaching in person, through skype, by phone, and at retreat locations. She offers VIP days that get you unstuck, focused, and into action.

If you do not have someone inspiring, uplifting, supporting and holding a bigger vision for you than you hold for yourself, you will benefit greatly from the one-on-one coaching with Diane.

This is the program to get intense feedback, personalized research, step-by-step training, and accountability. We will be generating ideas, fixing broken places, thinking of taglines, researching your competition, and helping you to "move the needle".

With her background as a counselor and now as a "business therapist", she helps you work through challenges, mindset struggles, and unhealthy business habits. We create a strategic solution-focused action plan for success in your marketing and your mindset. And we pray at the beginning and end of every session.

The type of client that she loves to work with is:

- An action taker
- Willing to try new things
- Committed to working through the discomfort of change and growth
- On a mission to build the business that God has given them
- Ready to let go of mistaken beliefs and mindsets

Are you ready to get started and discuss the right program for you?

Go to www.nacwe.org/getstarted and fill out the form or email diane@dianecunningham.com.

Are you ready to get started with coaching? Go to www.nacwe.org/getstarted and fill out the information form. You will then meet with Diane to discuss the options for private coaching or a VIP Day.

© 2010-2013 Diane Cunningham Companies LLC